FOSSETT'S MEMORY

FOSSETT'S MEMORY

by

CHRISTOPHER HOLLIS

Author of

DEATH OF A GENTLEMAN: THE LETTERS OF ROBERT FOSSETT

HOLLIS AND CARTER LTD.
25 ASHLEY PLACE
LONDON
S.W.1

First Published in 1944
Reprinted July, 1945

THIS BOOK IS PRODUCED IN
COMPLETE CONFORMITY WITH
THE AUTHORIZED ECONOMY STANDARDS

Printed in Great Britain by
Billing and Sons Ltd., Guildford and Esher

FOSSETT'S MEMORY

In the summer of 1943 I published a volume, entitled *Death of a Gentleman*, containing the fictional letters of Robert Fossett. While many kind things were said to me about that book, a friend made one day the complaint that it was depressing. Fossett, he said, was a good man and he stood for good things, but by the end of the book Fossett was dead and there was little hint that the good things for which he stood were not dying with him. This book is an attempt to answer that complaint—an attempt to show how death, even though it be premature, does not necessarily mean that life has been pointless.

It will be obvious that the mind of the fictional autobiographer of this book, Peter Hartington-Smith, is one that is developing throughout the book and still far from fixed and clear by the end of it. May I be allowed, then, to assure the reader that he must not assume that any political or religious opinions expressed by Peter Hartington-Smith are necessarily those of

CHRISTOPHER HOLLIS.

I

My brother-in-law, Robert Fossett, country squire, county cricketer, Conservative Member of Parliament, was killed fighting in the defence of Calais in May, 1940. He was then aged forty-four. He left behind him a widow, my sister, and three children—Martin, aged sixteen, Margaret, aged thirteen, and Robert, aged eleven.

I was at that time disguised in uniform in one of the Public Relations purlieus of the War Office, hiding shrinkingly behind the title of Captain. A few days after the news had come through I met Bobby's old school-fellow from Eton days, Anthony Arbuthnot. We went together to the Club for a glass of sherry.

'A bit tough about Bobby,' said Tony.

The drinks were brought and the waiter remunerated.

'And for your sister too,' he added.

I agreed in an embarrassed mumble.

'Seems such a waste,' he went on.

The conversation spaced itself through the pauses, as is the way of conversation after bereavement, when it does not seem decent to talk about anything but the dead; and yet what more is there to say after sorrow has been recorded? At last we found, each of us to his relief, that we had somehow drifted into another topic, and there we held ourselves with all the animation of escape. We exchanged gossip for half an hour, as if the old times were still with us, and then parted.

There stayed with me Tony's phrase, 'Seems such a waste.' Tony himself was no deep philosopher, filled with high vision of the destiny and vocation of man. His answers would not have been lucid had one asked him what made life a waste and what made it fruitful, nor was it perhaps easy to see why dying for one's country was a more culpable form of extravagance than drinking gin and Italian in Pall Mall clubs, which was the only other form of existence with which Tony was acquainted. Yet the phrase stuck with me on its intrinsic merits.

I was a supporter of the war, and therefore, if the war must be fought, I had to agree that people must be killed in it. Yet was it not a waste that a mind and a character, to whose formation such pains had been given, should be thus snuffed out? Men learnt in youth in order to do in middle age, and, if middle-age was denied to them, then the learning had proved, it seemed, a wholly fruitless travail. Ripeness was all, and, if there was not ripeness, all was nothing.

It was this immaturity in it which had seemed to me the outrage in the death of my eldest boy, David, in 1931. Our first children were twins, born in 1929. Ever since I was a boy at school I had been haunted by the beauty of that lovely line at the end of the Fourth Eclogue:

Incipe, parve puer, risu cognoscere matrem.

It may seem almost a silly confession from one who has no pretensions to be either a literary man or a classical scholar, but I think that I tell the truth when I say that my desire to have children, ever since I at all understood what having children meant, was to a large extent produced by, and almost entirely expressed by, that line. There is an overwhelming beauty in the inarticulate. The child, not yet able to speak, drags himself to his feet by his mother's knee, turns instinctively to hide his face on her breast from prying and admiring strangers, and begins, as Virgil says, to know his mother with a smile. Because there is no reasoning and because there are no words, there is therefore a meaning beyond reasoning and beyond words.

So no one was ever a prouder father than I when some fifteen years ago twins were born to us—a boy and a girl.

But two years later tragedy followed joy, and our boy, David, who had never been strong or healthy, died. It was the terrible commentary on my Virgilian love that the only smile with which he recognised his mother was a dying smile. It was the first real sorrow of my life, and my first reaction to that sorrow, at the time, was one of sheer revolt. It was with a similar revolt that I met Bobby's death. The waste seemed the more outrageous because forty years had been allowed to growth instead of only two. At the time of David's death I used to read a lot of Euripides because I thought he was Left and a mocker of the gods and translated by Gilbert Murray and everything else that an up-to-date Greek dramatist ought to be. One day in the *Andromache* I read that the best thing in life was to have children, but the next best thing was, not having them, to want them. Only he who did not even want them was past redemption. 'Children are the soul of life to all men,' writes Euripides, 'and, whoever complains because he has them not, by his complaints suffers the less and is so far blest in his unhappiness.' This seemed to me from experience to be true. Even in the agony of David's death I was still glad that he had been born. I did not say, and did not wish to say, 'The Lord gave, and the Lord hath taken away; blessed be the name of the Lord.' The loss was outrageously an evil against which I rebelliously complained. If it was perhaps 'better to have loved and lost than never to have loved at all,' that was not because the loss had any meaning, but only because the love was so good that even the memory of it was better than nothing. But at least I was 'blest in my unhappiness,' and, if no more than this was true, the wise philosopher would have asked what became of an easy Epicurean philosophy which found happiness only in the satisfaction of impulses and the absence of worry. Had it not proved itself inadequate? To that I had no answer, and, not being as yet a reasoner, I did not seriously attempt an answer. I left it to time to heal the wound and bury the conundrum in oblivion. And so the death of Bobby caught me again as completely bereft of a philosophy and an answer as had the death of David.

There were of course the religious consolations. I respected them. I could understand the man, and still more the woman, who would gladly accept less than the due in this life, confident that the just God would repay in the future. But I was quite certain that I did not then believe in any such equation. What reason was there to believe that there would be justice there save that there was injustice here? Even to-day, although I am much more sceptical of scepticism than I was those few years ago, I am not quite sure whether I believe in the equation. Anyhow, whether hopes of a future life be real or unreal, it was not on them that my mind dwelt as I debated whether Bobby's life should be called wasted, nor is it on the religious plane that I am trying to answer the question even now.

His death was more than an irrelevant accident. He stood for a way of life, for a form of ordering society. He was 'the last, sad squire' who rode 'slowly towards the sea,' and it seemed, and indeed it still seems, as if not only Robert Fossett but that whole order was dying in those weeks at Calais and on the beaches of Dunkirk. It was not only the Death of a Gentleman; it was the death of all gentlemen. Those who would survive could no longer narrow their appeal. Survival was only possible, if all were called in and all distinctions obliterated.

I was myself at that time a more or less conventional Left-Winger, denouncing appeasement, rejoicing that Mr. Chamberlain had fallen, welcoming the new brooms of Socialist salvation—Mr. Greenwood without a portfolio, Mr. Morrison with ever so many of them, all this and

Bevin too. Here, too, time has perhaps a little mellowed me into scepticism, and I am now no longer as sure of anything as I was then sure of everything. But at the time I thought that the order of the Fossetts was going out and that its death was both desirable and inevitable. A life lived for its preservation was, however disinterested, yet a wasted life; a death died for such a cause was only justified in so far as he who made the sacrifice was used for a purpose other than he intended or he guessed. The years have been needed in order to make me qualify my judgment.

I am no author—not even much of a letter-writer. I write primarily in order to clear my own mind. I have written down here a sort of book that is not often written about any man—but one that should perhaps be written more often both about the great and the undistinguished. I have written the Posthumous Life of Robert Fossett, the story of how he lived on in others after his death. It will not be a book that can be published—probably not a book that any other eye than mine can ever see. But the first purpose of writing is not to be read. The first purpose of writing is to clear one's own mind. Reading is mostly a waste of time.

II

In the middle of June, a little more than a month after Bobby's death, I got a week-end's leave and went down to Barston to see my sister Ruth, 'to talk things over' at her earnest request. All at the Manor House was, I found, in some confusion—that second condition of confusion after bereavement when tears have given place to packing-cases. The two younger children were at home, but Ruth pushed them off after tea and we settled down to our talk.

'The first thing to get clear, my dear,' I said, 'is how are you left?'

'And it's very hard to get it clear exactly,' said Ruth, 'but it's clear enough in the broad—very badly. Bobby never would have a regular solicitor. He said that lawyers ruined their minds by concentration on petty little points of no intrinsic interest and neglecting the great philosophic truths, and barristers proved how boring their life was by the fact that they could never talk about it except in terms of the money that they earned.'

'Good God,' I said. I had not come down to criticise Bobby, and it was neither the company nor the occasion to do so, but I could not quite restrain myself. It was typical of him, as, indeed, of all the Fossetts, never to act save through the invocation of some extraordinary general principle. 'Whoever pays a solicitor for his mind? One pays him for his attention. If you want to be a philosopher yourself, I should have thought it an admirable plan to pay somebody else to ruin his philosophical digestion rather than to ruin your own.'

'Exactly,' said Ruth; 'but then, you know, he did not like middle-men in anything. He thought that free men should market their own goods and manage their own affairs.'

'In any event,' I said, 'let us come to the brutal point, which is how much money have you got?"

'Easy to come to that,' said Ruth, with a light laugh. 'I have not got any. Funny, isn't it?'

A shaft of sunlight struck through the french window and fell on the keyboard of the piano. Ruth got up, walked across the room and, sitting down on the stool, started an idle strumming. 'Honest?' I asked, still sprawled out in my easy-chair. Again she laughed..

'Oh no,' she said, 'not quite absolutely, literally, honestly penniless, if by penniless you mean without a penny. You know how people talk about having no money. When Uncle Dotty told me that he was ruined in the slump and would have to give up everything, it turned out in fact that he knocked off taking the *Daily Sketch* for the servants to read in the kitchen.'

'And having wine for lunch when there weren't any guests,' I said. 'He was always most insistent about that.'

'Yes,' said Ruth, 'but as he was also equally insistent that there should always be guests, it did not make very much difference.'

'The only effect that the war has had on him so far,' I said, 'is that he has engaged an extra man-servant to look after the ration books.'

'Yes,' said Ruth, 'he's very patriotic. He won't employ anyone who did not have a good record in the last war. He thinks it almost a disgrace that Bobby waited till this one to get killed in.'

We neither of us had much regard or affection for our portentous, selfish and wealthy uncle, who aired upon nephews and nieces those graces with which during many years of Colonial Governorship he had been wont to impress His Majesty's dusky subjects. But this last sentence was a little near the bone. It was clear—as, indeed, I later learnt—that Uncle Dotty had been pressing his infelicitous pomposities in language that had aroused resentment. It was not the time to ask for details. I said nothing.

'In any event,' Ruth said, 'and seriously, I am poor in a very different sense to any in which Uncle Dotty was ever poor.'

'Meaning?' I asked.

'Meaning,' she said, 'death-duties to pay, and then a very few hundreds a year—it may be three, it may be five, it may be somewhere between.'

'Say four,' I said, fatuously feeling, I cannot imagine why, that it was somehow funny.

'For the sake of argument,' she agreed. 'Anyway there it is, somewhere in the happy mean between Uncle Dotty and the doss-house.'

'And why has it turned out as bad as this?'

'Oh, for a variety of reasons,' she answered; 'most of them rather to Bobby's credit. It all began with the perambulator canopies. He went into them in the 1920's with the idea that he could make some money there that could compensate for making nothing out of the estate. So he did as long as the 1920's were on. Then with the slump prices fell and demand fell, and of course the right capitalist answer was to reduce wages and to turn off hands. But Bobby never would do either of those things. He said that the labour for his factory all came from one little town and that he was the only factory employer in that town. Therefore it would be false economy to have his labour demoralised by dole and idleness in order to save a few shillings, particularly as the workers there are all women. If he did that, they would be neither willing nor able to help him regain markets when better times came. So he kept them on and kept up their wages, and as a result, of course, the firm ceased to make a profit.'

'It's a devilish difficult conundrum where your duty towards your employee ends and your duty towards your family begins,' I said.

I remembered very well my last talk with Bobby one day in London during his embarkation leave. He had been then singularly light-hearted about the practical problems of income and the family by which most of us are always so greatly oppressed. He always was light-hearted when he was quite sure that he had done right. He had a touchingly literal belief in the parable of the lilies of the field—a belief that one so often does find in spiritual men who have an independent income. Either, he had argued, things would get better or they would get worse. If they got better, then he would be able to get straight again, and, if they got worse, then none of these dodges and reductions would save one's money anyway. It was not worth while twisting and tricking and turning so as to keep a bank balance for a year or two more. It was better to behave decently, he had argued; and decent behaviour, even if it made no money, might possibly save one from a lamp-post.

'Oh no,' I had answered, 'revolutionaries always hang their best friends.'

He agreed.

He had always found that the opponent of decent wages was the manager. The manager could not get it out of his head that his employer would judge his efficiency by his success in reducing wages, and, when Bobby assured him that this was not so, the manager thought he was a lunatic.

Ruth and I were walking after dinner in the orchard. It was a lovely summer evening. There had been rain a day or two before, just enough of it to keep the scent alive, and I had taken my walk that way because, for all that I knew, it would be the last time that I would ever walk in Barston orchard. I knew that it was Ruth's favourite walk, too. Orchards always are a favourite with women. Have you ever noticed how all the best things that have ever been said about apple trees have been said by women—Christina Rossetti, George Eliot, Sappho—Eve, for all I know?

'Bobby,' broke in Ruth on our silence, 'always had a great bee in his bonnet about gentlemen behaving like gentlemen. He thought that in every society there was always a governing class and that from time to time one governing class went out and another came in. It was likely enough that the present would prove to be such a time. If so, he had no sort of bitterness about it. He was anything but a die-hard, but the important thing was to go out like a gentleman.'

'And so he did, my dear,' I said as gently as I could. 'But how does that help this particular problem?'

It was in truth my opinion that it was a magnificent folly, even if the folly of a gentleman, for a family man like Bobby to take so much trouble to get himself killed at a time when every yard of red tape in Whitehall was devoted to prevent him from doing so; but this was hardly the moment to say as much.

> Oh, stay with company and mirth
> And daylight and the air;
> Too full already is the grave
> Of fellows that were good and brave
> And died because they were,

I could have cried with Housman. But to what purpose now that it was all too late?

'Of course we could have pulled things together with the war to some extent,' said Ruth. 'Farmers could pay their rents again, and the Government talked about using the canopy factory for making parachutes. I expect that it will by the end of the war, and it is possible that before the war is through there will really be some money coming out of that. But at present everything is in the mess-up which there always is whenever the Government tries to run anything. The Government commandeered the factory, and, in order to use it for parachutes, they needed to install some new machinery. Then of course there was a row between the Ministry of This and the Ministry of That about the machinery, and to this day it hasn't been installed. The factory has been used neither for making canopies nor for making parachutes, and the Treasury won't pay any compensation until the new machinery is installed, and the Ministry of Supply say that they can't install it until the Treasury has paid. I dare say that if

Bobby had been about he could have got it all straightened out. But then he was not about. He was in France living on a private's pay. But anyway I don't know that it much matters.'

'It seems to me that it does matter a good deal, my dear,' I said.

We had got back to the front lawn, and I was busying myself with collecting some stumps and bats that the children had left lying about.

'Well, don't you think Bobby was right?' she asked. 'Naturally enough, it is all against the grain for a woman to pay much attention to arguments up in the air like that. We are concrete and "of the earth, earthy," but one can't very well help attending to it with the world as it is now.'

'Right about what?' I asked. 'He had so many opinions.'

'I mean, right about thinking that things would either get better or else go right down the drain. What difference can it make in this summer of 1940 whether one is left £400 a year or £4,000 a year or £40,000 a year? Does anyone seriously suppose that we shall own any of it a year from now? Why, the Germans entered Paris yesterday. What do you really think is going to happen in this war? Hang it all, Peter, you're in the War Office. Even you must have heard of the war.'

'Vaguely,' I agreed with a polite smile, as I lit a cigarette.

'Well, and what do you think about it? Have your secret documents got anything in them which contradicts my impression?'

'I will tell you exactly what I think about the war,' I said after pondering for a minute. 'The secret documents—the very mildly secret documents—that I have seen are all on your side. All the facts and statistics seem to bear you out that we shall be beaten, and, if I had to argue it out with some well-informed person, he would be able to make at least four or five points in favour of our defeat to which I could not give an honest answer. And yet, somehow, I don't believe that we will be beaten. It is not merely that I won't say that we will be beaten, but I don't believe it.'

'But why not?' asked Ruth. 'That is just what I am trying to get at.'

'I wish that I knew,' I answered; 'but I believe that it is just failure of imagination. Bobby used to argue about miracles and things like that that the balance of the argument was very often in favour of them, and people refused to believe simply because the demand was too great for their imagination. I don't know if he was right about miracles, but I think that that is an exact description of the mentality of an Englishman threatened with the loss of a war. We never have lost a war, we never have been invaded, for so many centuries, that, whatever the statistics may show, we just cannot believe that we will lose this one. We know that we can lose battles, of course, and even campaigns. We have done that often enough before. But what of them? Their loss only means that the war will be rather longer than we had thought, but, as we had never had any idea how long it would be anyway, that does not really greatly worry us. But we still assume, however black things look at the moment, that we are bound to win in the end.'

'Perhaps so,' said Ruth; 'but, if so, then by your own confession your opinion is not a very valuable one.'

'Oh yes, it is,' I said. 'It may show that I am a bloody fool, but the fact that I am a bloody fool is one of the factors in the situation. Haven't you ever read William James?'

'No, I haven't,' said Ruth.

'Nor Virgil, I suppose,' I added sadly. 'Women don't.'

'Of course I've read Virgil,' she said. 'I'm not quite illiterate.'

'Well,' I said, '*possunt quia posse videntur*. Or take M. Coué. Don't you see that the fact that Englishmen think that they are going to win is one of the main reasons why they do win? Other nations enter into a war with a feeling that it is about even money whether they win or lose. So, when they have lost a campaign, they begin to count the cost and to consider whether it would not be a good plan to pack up. Englishmen, when they have lost a campaign, just go on until they have won a campaign; so they do win. They're too stupid to know when they're beaten.'

'Yes, there's something in that,' said Ruth. 'Of course we —you and I—are spoiled for the complete English self-confidence by our Kentucky blood. That brings in a strain of the noblest causes, yet destined to defeat. *Victrix causa deis placuit, sed victa Catoni*, and all that.'

'It does to you,' I said, 'but I don't think that it does to me. We are different in that.'

'Whatever the future,' I put in as my parting shot from the stairs as we went to bed, 'the only practical plan is to behave as if the world was still going on—both in your private and public affairs. Then, if it does go on, you are provided for, and, if the Day of Judgment comes instead, you won't cut any worse a figure there for having still been sane the day before its arrival.'

'But Bobby used always to say . . .' began Ruth.

'Oh yes, my dear, but Bobby was always rather a one for ancestral voices prophesying woe.'

'It's war,' said Ruth, 'not woe.'

'Oh, is it?' I said. 'Well, of course that's easier—betting on a certainty.'

I was up early next morning—one of those mornings when one goes out into the garden in one's pyjamas before breakfast and vaguely hopes that somebody will be shocked. I was smoking a cigarette and aimlessly gazing at the play of water in the sun in the fountain on the middle of the lawn. Ruth came up behind me.

'Aren't you taking any breakfast this morning?' she asked.

The answer to the question was so evident that no answer was required.

'What are you going to do with your £400 a year?' I asked.

'I will tell you exactly,' said Ruth. 'I am going to farm. Billy Bourne at Tinker's Farm is going to be called up—or at least is going to join up. So we are all to move in there. We could not stay in this house anyway. I haven't the money, and I could not find the servants, even if I had the money. I think that the military will take this place over—officers, I am afraid, so, of course, they will kick it to pieces, which will make my heart a bit sad. But *que voulez-vous*? Then I shall farm Billy Bourne's land. The children of course are the problem. I do not so much mind about the younger ones. Robert is only eleven and, as things are now, I would just as soon have him under my eye and at the village school, at any rate for a term or two, until we can see both how my budget is making out and what is happening about this invasion.'

'It's a very good thing to talk about unconventional ways of educating your children,' I said. 'It broadens the mind—provided, of course, that you do in the end educate them quite conventionally.'

'And then Margaret does not matter so much,' she continued. 'I do not believe in all this education for women. She can go into Castle Cary to the High School for a year or two and then come and help full-time on the farm and in the house. It will do her far more good than passing a lot of silly examinations. But Martin, I admit, is rather a problem. Sixteen is too early for him to leave school and too late for him to go to another school. He is at rather a difficult age, and I don't want him to be one of those horrid young men with a grievance against life. It does not in many ways very much matter what sort of a school a boy goes to, but it does very much matter that he should not be jiggered about from one sort of school to another.'

I had come prepared for this. I was not then—and still less am I now—a rich man, and I had a wife and three children to provide for. Still, the younger children were not yet of school age, and indeed, though we had not at that time made the decision, they all were soon to be taken off our hands, in the sense that (most mistakenly) we were to send them to our Kentucky relatives. As long as they were there we were not, of course, allowed by the regulations of the British Government to contribute to their support. I agreed with my brother-in-law at any rate to the extent that it was no longer sensible carefully to save money for future emergencies. If there was good to be done with it immediately, it was best used so. At the moment I had a little more money than my sister, and before I had come down to Barston my wife and I had agreed that, if the family council should show that she needed assistance and that there was any way in which we could give it without offensiveness, we should not hold back. Besides, whether Bobby's gesture was magnificent or not, at least it was the war. He was dead, and death is always dignified, if only because those who live can never be quite certain that they could face it. I had all the feeling of inferiority—all the feeling that I owed a debt which the man who stayed at home must always have in common decency—the more so perhaps if he stayed at home in uniform. This seemed the opportunity.

'Don't worry about Martin, Ruth dear,' I said. 'Of course it would be a disaster to take him away from school just now and rob him of his last year or two. Public-school life is a balanced whole, and the beginning is all designed to lead on to the end. If you don't have the last year, with all its funny little responsibilities and privileges and swankings-about, then you can't even get the retrospective benefit out of the first years. Men can see that better than women. We will be responsible for seeing Martin through Trumpinghurst. I talked it all over with Marjorie, and she quite agrees. After all, I am his godfather.'

My sister Ruth was never one to greet with the pantomime insincerities of 'Oh, I really couldn't' an offer which she had every intention of accepting. She had her pride and she had the limitations to her pride. She decided at once when she was going to accept and when she was going to refuse a proposition, and stated at once her refusal or acceptance.

'Thanks awfully, Peter,' she said. 'You are a brick. If you are really quite sure that you mean it and quite sure that Marjorie agrees, I don't pretend that I'll say No to that. Perhaps I may be able to pay back some day, if we ever get this compensation business with the canopies straightened out. But frankly I would rather not make any promises about that, because you know what the Government is.'

'Oh, that's all right,' I agreed.

'And, Peter,' she went on, 'it is not really only a matter of signing cheques. Sixteen is rather a difficult age, and I suppose that seventeen and eighteen and nineteen will be more difficult still. It is like asking a boy to go through life with a leg off to ask him to go through those years without a father—and Bobby and Martin were getting on particularly well. I should be most grateful if you could take some chance to get to know him and to keep an eye on how he is developing. A man can understand so many things about that that a woman cannot.'

I agreed to this, too, though less certain how I should fulfil my promise.

'And as for the other two,' I said, 'I think it best for me not to promise more than I can perform, and I'm afraid that I just can't take on any more, if I am going to do Martin. But if you find that you can't manage anything, when you have had time to look round, well, then Uncle Dotty will just have to stump up.'

'What a hope!' said Ruth. 'But honestly about Margaret, I really don't mind. That is not just a question of sour grapes. I do really very strongly disapprove of education for women. And as for Robert, we will have to wait to see how things turn out. It does not really so much matter about him because he has not seriously started his away-from-home education yet.'

'Boys of eleven seem to me to have a perfect career as Professors of Basic English,' I said. 'It's just the way that they talk.'

'His education can be the same all through, at any rate,' said Ruth.

'All right, that's settled, then,' I said. 'And how about the work? Do you think that you can manage that?'

'Oh yes, that'll be as easy as falling off a log,' said Ruth. 'Farm work is all a question whether one was brought up to it or not, and we were all born in the pig-sty and reared in a haystack.'

'How extremely surprised Mother would be to hear it,' I protested. 'Still, I see what you mean.'

'And then I can trust the people down here to see me through,' she went on. 'That is the dividend we get out of Bobby always being so decent to them and—what's more—so friendly with them. If a cash-nexus-man, like Uncle Dotty, tries to buy himself into favour with village people by just giving them things and money, they take what he gives but they pay him back no thanks in return. And, if he should then come to lose his money, they are just angry with him for losing the only thing about him that could conceivably be of value to anybody else. But with a friend like Bobby it is different. To men like Billy Perkins, if Bobby hits hard times or if we hit hard times because of Bobby's death, then they are just like Highlanders to their chieftains after the '45. They think that it is up to them to help to see us through.'

'Well, that's to be proved,' I said, for I had all the conventional left-winger's scepticism about the decency of the poor.

'Bobby had strong principles about money, even when we owned some. He thought that nobody had a right to spend more than necessary on himself and his family, however much he owned. You never noticed our economy, because hospitality was one of the things on which he thought that one ought to spend. So you always had good wine and plenty of it. But, when it was only the family, it was always water. He thought there was something barbaric about luxury. He was a bit of a prig about that. The villagers, of course, thought it dotty of him not to drink more. Yet they liked it because it meant that he could be more generous in money with them.'

'Oh,' I said, 'it's very difficult to know what they really think of the conventional squire. Armstrong, for instance. . . .'

'Bobby was anything but the conventional squire,' said Ruth.

This was indeed true. 'Fox-hunting' seems almost the inevitable epithet for a squire, and Bobby never hunted a fox in his life. He refused to preserve pheasants.

'He hated killing things,' said Ruth

'But he wasn't against blood-sports,' I said.

'He wasn't against killing things,' said Ruth. 'He only hated it. He was not a lunatic or a townee humanitarian. He understood what was necessary. He always used to argue that there was a good deal to be said for Macaulay's

Puritan, who objected to bear-baiting, not because it gave pain to the bear, but because it gave pleasure to the spectator. He was against fox-hunting and in favour of fox-shooting. Yet his main argument against pheasant-shooting was not that it meant the destruction of pheasants but that it meant the destruction of everything else. For the sake of the pheasants, weazels, badgers, sparrowhawks, buzzards, goshawks, roe-deer, even foxes, have to be destroyed. The people must be prevented from wandering off the paths and stopped from picking up a piece or two of dead wood, as they had always been allowed to do from time immemorial.'

'Don't you tell me that the country people mind pheasant-preserving,' I protested. 'They are all for it. It brings some money into the country in October and November, which is just the time when there is very little doing there.'

'And don't you tell me that they don't mind it,' said Ruth. 'That is just the mistake that the townees make. They think that because the country people take money, therefore gratitude can be bought. I tell you it can't. They only count you as a human being if you really share their life, and it's only when they feel like that they think that any personal obligations even begin.'

By then we had drifted into the breakfast-room, and Bertha had brought in coffee and bacon and eggs for us.

'And what are you going to do about servants?' I asked.

'Oh, it's the same sort of principle there,' said Ruth. 'There are two sorts of servants—those one can't keep and those one can't get rid of. There would be no question of our being able to afford more than one anyway, and Bertha just took it for granted that she was coming with us, before anyone ever had a chance of saying a word.'

'Well, my dear,' I said, unable to suppress some admiration at her courage and optimism, 'you seem to have got it all remarkably well taped, I must say.'

It is natural for a woman to be reliant upon others. But for that very reason when a good woman is compelled to face life without support, the courage and the gaiety with which she does so are amazing.

III

At the beginning of the next August I had a week's leave, which by the customary judicious annexation of an extra forty-eight hours I was able to transform into ten days. It was a curious time to be taking leave, while London and all England was waiting for the great assault, for which the small preliminary raids over the provinces in June and July seemed to be the preparation. But as no one knew when or whether he would have leave again, we were advised to take it as we could, taking it of course under a very real and present possibility of recall. Marjorie and I occupied the first day of it seeing our own children off from Liverpool to America—Elizabeth, David's surviving twin, and Monica and Christopher, four and six years her junior. Then we went to spend the rest of it at Barston, to see how Ruth was adjusting herself and her family to the new life.

I had previously walked past Tinker's Farm but had never before paid any detailed attention to it. It was, I found now, a pleasant place, a long, low Cromwellian farmhouse with all its farm buildings attached behind it. It was strictly for work, and a box-hedge shut in the tiniest of flower gardens, which was all that relaxation was allowed to rescue from agriculture. A little stone-flagged path ran up from the gate to an old, handsome, simple doorway, with an arch on top of it. There was a deep, dark-red roof, clouded with lichen and moss, from among which yellow stonecrop winked out at the visitor.

Margaret, aged thirteen, had come out to meet us at the gate, and, brushing aside preliminary greetings or inquiries, at once plunged into an easy prattle about the topics which in August, 1940, seemed to her the most important in the world.

'Do you know what that is?' she asked Marjorie.

'Why, that's the roof,' Marjorie answered.

'No, no,' said Margaret, impatient at such trifling or such stupidity, 'that yellow flower on the roof.'

'Yes,' said Marjorie, 'that's stonecrop.'

'Ah,' said Margaret, 'but do you know what the village people call it?'

'No,' we said. What did they call it?

'Hands says,' proudly announced Margaret, rather as if she were a B.B.C. official declaring an armistice, 'that it's called Welcome-Home-Husband-However-Drunk. And do you know what those are called?' she said, pointing to a large tub of flowers by the side of the path.

They were pansies, and we said as much.

'Hands says,' the voice repeated, 'that they're called Kiss-Me-John-At-The-Garden-Gate.'

Hands, we soon discovered, was a curious old character, half odd-job man, half shepherd, and was for the moment the leading educational influence in Margaret's life and, to a lesser extent, in that of her younger brother, Robert. He was a very tall, very brown old man, with curious sunken, piercing eyes. Indeed, he reminded me somewhat incongruously of Dante's description of St. John the Evangelist—'an old man alone with piercing visage in a trance'—*'Un vecchio solo, dormendo, con la fascia arguta.'* He was, we were confidently told, even more learned than Billy

Perkins, the cowman, nor was it the least of his claims to distinction that not only was he himself but he was also the uncle of Tom.

Two of the village boys, we were soon to learn, had once captured a sitting titlark—it may have been yesterday, it may have been a thousand years ago; these tales were always dateless and indeed outside time, like an old Greek myth. They had then quarrelled over the possession of it. While they were quarrelling, Hands had reached out with his stick and picked off the hat, so that the titlark could fly away.

It was Hands again who explained that, though it was perhaps illegal, it was not immoral for a hard-working man to pick up an odd hare, or rabbit, or wounded partridge that he might come across, but that to be a regular poacher and to depend for your livelihood on the products of poaching rather than on honest work was despicable. 'Any-one might take a rabbit now and again,' he said, 'but a regular poacher's no good.' He had spoken '*urbi et orbi* on a matter of faith and morals and to the whole world,' and Margaret made it abundantly clear that there Rome had spoken and the cause was finished. All arguments about poaching were refuted with the firm repetition of Hands' dictum.

It was Hands, too, who explained the best of all ways of catching hares. He used to make a hare's form, and make it so skilfully that neither man nor hare would have guessed it to be of human contrivance. Then he went the rounds, accompanied by his dog Paunch and carrying his shepherd's crook. Wherever he found a form filled, he would give a word to Paunch, who would sit down in front of the hare and occupy it in watching her. Meanwhile Hands himself would make a wide and silent circle until he came within range of the hare from behind and was able to kill it with a blow of his crook. Margaret had been allowed to watch this manœuvre in strictest silence and from a distance, and one day she might be allowed to attempt a circle herself. This tracking, Hands said, was far superior to trapping, though it was possible to catch hares in a trap, provided only that you remembered that hares loved the smell of blackthorn and therefore tied the trap to a blackthorn twig.

It was Hands again who explained that on the lands on which sheep fed the grasses and clover and herbs all grew close to the ground, because sheep nibbled so close to the ground that the clovers learnt to grow thus as the only hope of escaping them. It was Hands again who explained that the greatest of all the evils of the fox-hunt was that the fox was apt to take refuge among the ewes and the hounds to follow it. If the ewes were with lamb the commotion so terrified them that they delivered prematurely.

His, too, the authority which told them that there used to be bustards in Somerset but that there were now bustards no longer, that there was no known way of keeping the rooks from the stooks at harvest-time, that the sparrowhawk was so dainty a feeder that in summer, when the breeding birds were abundant, he would never eat the body of his victim. He would peck off the head, swallow it whole after removing the beak, but leave the body on the ground.

Yet, as I say, Hands' most considerable claim to fame was his uncledom of Tom. Tom I was to be shown on my second morning at Barston. He was a pleasant-looking, light-haired, lanky youth of about eighteen, with a cloth cap perched a little loutishly on the back of his head so that a broad fringe of his hair protruded from it. He was seated in the front of the waggon, which the two farm horses, Dot and Carry, were dragging back with the first stooks of the harvest. A cigarette lolled out of the left corner of his mouth. There was, I must confess, but little mark of greatness in his aspect. Yet a great person he was, great, as Margaret told me, not like his uncle, because of his learning and his opinions, but because of his achievements. These were many, and of them the most marvellous was his capture of the chaffinch's nest. Here again, as with so many of the feats of Margaret's heroes, I could never clearly discover whether this was something that Margaret had herself seen or an exploit of the legendary past.

'Do you know how Tom got the chaffinch's nest?' she asked me. 'It was up in that fir tree, and the other boys said that no one could get it unless they went home and fetched a ladder. But Tom said he would climb up and get it, and they said he couldn't, but he said he could, and they all bet him half a gallon of beer that he wouldn't. So he climbed up legs first without using his hands, and then came down again head first, holding the nest in his hand and only using his legs.'

Some achieve greatness. I myself was introduced both to Tom and to Hands, but I must confess that I did not myself ever get very much out of either of them. Margaret was at pains to make it clear to me that it would be folly to expect such a condescension. I must be content to learn of their greatness and their exploits through her intermediary.

Margaret and Robert made an amusing couple at their age. Children of the farm, there was about them an unsophisticated atmosphere of disinterested fecundity which I found attractive. Foaling and calving and lambing were the great excitements of their lives. 'Virgilian,' I remember that Bobby used to call it.

'Hands says that a donkey's period of gestation is thirteen months,' Margaret confided in me, as we grubbed in the hen-run for eggs.

'A human being's is only nine months,' chimed in Robert.

'But an elephant goes on for years and years,' Margaret added.

'Cocks don't lay eggs,' said Robert, with an air of finality.

In Bobby's time, and when they were squires rather than farmers, it had always been, I remembered, the family custom to ask round the breakfast-table at the time of haymaking and harvest, whether anybody was going to help that day. There was no compulsion. It was understood that the children were on holiday, and if they wanted to do something else, or if they wanted to do nothing, no objection was raised. With the hiling, as indeed—so Ruth told me—with everything else, each at its appropriate season, both around the farm and around the house, Margaret was of very real assistance. She worked through a whole long August day among the oats, hiling the stooks that were liberally interlaced with thistles, only breaking off at a quarter to four to do her milking, and bringing back her well-pricked fingers to the tap in the evening. Robert, though his assistance was not yet of very great practical value, yet followed the cutter round the field and gave comically grown-up advice to the indefatigable Billy Perkins.

'You should have put more lime down **here**, Mr. Perkins,' I heard him say. 'Needed more lime. I suppose it will have to go back to grass next year.'

Billy Perkins was loud in his praise of both of them, and prophesied that, when they grew up, they would be 'as good as I be myself'—the highest praise of which his generous soul was capable.

But Martin was not so interested in the crops. He went to the hiling in the morning, but without enthusiasm, and came away after about an hour. According to the custom of the house he had the right to do this, if he wished, and there was no rebuke.

The lawn by the walnut tree in the old Manor House was no longer theirs, but there was a tolerably level field just behind their farm. There the Fossetts had levelled and rolled out a cricket-pitch of a sort. The outfield was quite rough and even the pitch itself was of no Oval consistency. Still, it was good enough for some delightful family and village cricket. The sides were usually light-hearted and indeterminate. Passing callers, neighbours or the village men and boys drifted into and out of the opposing teams with easy carelessness, and the game went vaguely on until everyone decided that it had gone on long enough, and then it stopped.

We had an evening's game a couple of days after I arrived. It was a strange time for cricket, as the Luftwaffe gathered itself for its pounce across the Channel, but, if so strange, therefore the more precious. The declining sun threw long, dark shadows of the yew trees across the grass. A couple of cows grazed with exaggerated indifference in the outfield as if a little offended that they had not yet been picked for either side, while hens ran to and fro from third-man to long-leg with all the enthusiasm of the incompetent fielder, determined at least to be in his place. I still remember—it is one of those vignettes that stay stamped upon the mind when more important things have perished—plugging them down my medium left-handers. Tom, the shepherd's nephew, was batting and prepared to smite it lustily, but there was a spot in the pitch that was my good friend. The ball did not come through quite as expected. Tom tried to change his stroke too late, and he popped the ball up into the middle of the pitch. I was following up, shot out my right hand, just reached the ball and took it near the ground. It was a neat little catch, but, even had the game been of the first importance, it would not have been a memorable one, but it is extraordinary how great is the satisfaction of these little athletic achievements. They remain in the mind as memories and as consolations. I have heard that Dean Inge has somewhere said that life for him has had no keener pleasure than that of killing the ball at the net at tennis. If indeed he said this, then he was a most honest man.

I liked the way that Martin behaved in this cricket game. He was a lovely schoolboy cricketer—had all his father's cricket in him—that gorgeous, free, wristy off-drive through the covers and the true batsman's talent for playing back without a trace of hurry. He never slogged and never lifted the ball. One had but to see him bat an over and one knew that here was an incipient master. Now good cricketers of sixteen are sometimes something of a problem in the light-hearted family cricket matches. Either they take it too seriously, play too well, and spoil all the fun by hitting their juniors inordinately over the field. Or they overact absurdly—get themselves out much too obviously by hitting their wickets, drop catches which everyone can see that they could have held, and indulge in exaggerated lamentations when they are dismissed. But Martin avoided both the Scylla and the Charybdis of these difficulties most admirably. He was cheerful, laughing, but at the same time gave no evidence, notable to those younger than himself, that he did not take the game wholly seriously. He made some runs, but not too many, and, when he got out, he got out to difficult catches, which just possibly might not have been given on purpose. Indeed, to sisters, to ladies, to younger boys, he was cricket's very mirror of courtesy. He failed only, if failure it must be counted, in that he never thought that concessions need be made to middle-aged uncles out of practice—that they, too, a little trembled when the vigour of youth bumped them down too fast or had a vanity which might be flattered at being allowed to take a wicket, if it was not made too humiliatingly obvious that the wicket was thrown away on purpose.

My last visit to the Manor was for a snatched week-end in the middle of September. I wanted to see Ruth once more to review her finances. Billy Perkins asked me to come out and spend the evening with the Home Guard, who kept their watch on Carter's Hill. What an unforgettable evening it was! A lovely September night, one of those nights that is the more lovely because it bears upon it all the marks that it is the last of glory. It was the sort of day when in another year parents would be taking their children down to bathe with the thought that this perhaps was the last swim of summer and when 'the flannelled fool' lingers on in his white after the final set of tennis. 'I don't think that I will change back for dinner,' he says, not knowing when he will be in flannels again, and after dinner he sits out on an even lawn in the darkness in his deck-chair, having well tired the sun with talking and surrendering at last only to the gnats which drive him in to bed. So in another year, but this year four farmers—one of them a gentleman, three not—assembled together at a little caravan-hut on the hill-top, gazed down upon the sun setting at a port-town where two thousand years ago the Phœnician merchants came trafficking for tin, and scoured the plain for sight of a descending German parachutist. They had no arms. They had no uniform. At that date they had never suffered drill. I asked them what they were supposed to do if they saw a parachutist. They told me that they had to report him. I asked to whom. One said to Mr. Clothier, the mine-manager; another that it was to Cumbersome, the village schoolmaster. There was an argument about it, one saying one thing and the other the other, and the gentleman laughing a little and not pretending to know.

We sat on the steps of the caravan, arguing the point. Then we walked across the field so that one of the farmers could show me the new sort of fencing that they had put in there on the pretence that it would keep out the rabbits, and another pointed out where the best mushrooms grew and explained why. As we came back, the darkness was gathering and it was no longer easy to see a man's face.

We heard voices and saw in the dim two figures walk up the road, open the gate and come towards us along the track.

'It's Mr. Clothier come to inspect us,' said one of the farmers.

Clothier was making his evening round, bringing a guest with him. As they drew nearer we could see that their hands were lifted up and that they were shouting a little excitedly.

'Thumbs up,' shouted Clothier, as he came within range. 'Did you hear the nine o'clock news?'

We had not.

'A hundred and eighty-five,' he said.

'A hundred and eighty-five!' said one of the farmers incredulously.

The other two said nothing, but sucked at their pipes.

'I shouldn't wonder if that did really prove a turning-point,' said the gentleman. He did not quite know what he meant. None of us quite knew what he meant. Yet we all felt that what he said was true—as indeed it was.

A horse neighed in the next field and we heard some bird or animal rustling home in the nearby wood. The noise of a belated lorry came across the still valley from the quarry.

'It's peaceful enough here,' said one of the farmers, 'and yet I suppose that at this moment over London there's sweet merry hell itself.'

I could not help feeling that, though their part was not to be reckoned with that of the soldiers of Dunkirk or of the fighter pilots of the R.A.F., yet this most English army—so like the English armies at which Shakespeare and Dryden and Sheridan had mocked—had, too, its share in England's glory.

'I'm the get-away man,' said one of the farmers. 'When Hitler lands, George and Ernest have to crawl towards him on their stomachs with a bomb in one hand. But I have to run away and tell Mr. Cumbersome.'

'Oh, he'll never land,' said another. 'He's such a fidget.'

IV

I WAS not, as I have written in a previous chapter, inordinately apprehensive about the outcome of the war. I know how very foolish were my grounds for confidence, but I am making a record, not an apologia. I did not then believe that the aeroplane had changed the whole nature of warfare. I still thought that we had command of the sea and that so long as we had that command invasion was impossible. Aerial bombardment I thought of as a form of extended artillery. As support for an attacking army I did not doubt that it was important. By itself I thought that it was irrelevant, erratic and comparatively unimportant. I rejoiced when the great days of the Battle of Britain came, but I was not greatly surprised. It was what I had expected. I had always understood that aeroplanes could be shot down. It was not until many months later that I came to have any sort of inkling how narrow had been the margin of victory and what would have been the consequences of defeat.

The bombing of London I minded very little. I think that London is a horrible, ugly, sprawling place, and, if its vulnerability should cause the country's population to redistribute itself more sanely, that would be, I argued, an advantage. The æsthetic balance of the Battle of Britain was much more nearly even than it was the fashion to pretend. If some beautiful buildings were destroyed, so, too, were many more ugly ones. New vistas were opened up, unguessed at since the time of Wren and Inigo

Jones. It might indeed be pleaded that ugly buildings could be pulled down anyway without the aid of a bomb and that beautiful buildings could not be replaced. In theory this was doubtless true, but in practice, our public and municipal authorities being what they are, it had been found in the years before the war quite impossible to overcome the vested interests, which prevented the destruction of mean slums, and as impossible to save London's beautiful streets and buildings from renovation and desecration. Of all the public authorities which have laid their hand upon London in the last fifty years the Luftwaffe has been the least destructive.

Yet for all that, it may be answered, their method of destruction was not a pleasant one. I can only reply that, speaking for myself, recording and not defending, I found it so in September, 1940. As far as I minded anything, I minded people making a fuss about bombs far more than I minded bombs. Doubtless it was a certain lack of balance in the times which caused me to feel so. Doubtless it was just because Robert Fossett and other friends had been killed in France three months before, while I lingered in London, that I greeted with a certain compensating joy death when it came to London, too. But, however that may be, I did in the early days of September get a schoolboy's excitement out of the nightly bombing, and, as for death or wounds, somehow their reality had not yet come to my imagination. I knew that people got killed by bombs, that people were being killed by bombs. But it so happened that during this first month no one of my acquaintance was killed, and I assumed, as I listened to the whistle of the bombs night after night, that, however near they might come, they would not kill either me or my friends. When Uncle Dotty asked of the inmates of a house in which there had been casualties, 'Only the servants, I suppose?' I felt that the remark was sociologically obscene, as indeed it was, but I did not feel that the loss had been real. I treated raid accidents like road accidents. I knew that road accidents happened. I denounced them as intolerable, but I have never thought it possible that, when I cross a street, I myself will be knocked down by a motor-car. That civilians do not get killed in war seemed to me not so much a moral rule as a statement of fact. Foreign civilians, of course, were different, but it could not happen here. Even when it was happening I still fatuously felt that it could not happen here. Marjorie faced the blitz with the courage and gaiety with which all London faced it. She went four nights a week, when I was on duty in the War Office, to serve in a canteen in Islington. She went without a word of complaint and without a trace of fear, driving back sometimes through a street of fire. Yet, while she greeted the blitz with courage, she thought that it was a strain of obscene masochism in me which caused me to greet it with exultation. No one, she said, who had seen the blitz in the East End, its broken streets, could be excused for thinking it in any way amusing. I dare say that she was right. I was soon to have every reason for knowing that she was right.

It was one evening in late October—a dark, dank, chill, though fogless, evening. The worst of the blitz on London was over and the weight of the attack had switched to the provinces. Yet we still had our nightly alerts. I sat on duty at the War Office. It did not appear to be a night of heavy raiding. The telephone rang. I picked it up, expecting one of the boring routine inquiries. It was a private call. The line was very indistinct. 'Yes, this is Captain Hartington-Smith.' And gradually through repetition and confusion the indistinct words pieced themselves together into their dreadful pattern. It was one of my wife's fellow-workers at the canteen. A lone bomb had fallen on the shelter beneath the canteen. Twenty people had been killed instantly—my wife among them.

'Thanks,' I said, and put down the receiver. There was nothing else to be said.

I stared stupidly across at the map on the wall. A rat scuttled across behind it as rats were apt to do. I thought inanely of 'rats that leave the sinking ship.' My colleague put a cup of tea by my side. I paid no attention.

'Do you mind if I go now?' I said, rousing myself as if from sleep.

'Go?' he said. 'Where do you want to go to? The alert's still on, you know.'

'My wife's just been killed,' I said. 'That's what that call was about.'

'Oh, I'm awfully sorry,' he said.

We did not know one another particularly well.

I got up, put on my hat and coat, took my gas-mask and stumbled vaguely out into the night, intent on finding the way to Islington. But it was all too late.

> She should have died hereafter;
> There would have been a time for such a word.

How right Macbeth was to know that the moment of battle was not a moment for obituary notices! The flames light up a world of fantastic unreality, and death is the great reality. It is for quiet contemplation—not for confusion.

Of the meaning to me of that loss, of the loss of a perfect companion by a young man whose whole being was made for companionship, of the loss after only twelve years of marriage and with the children four thousand miles away across the Atlantic, I will not attempt to speak even now. Language can only speak of relations and of universals—can classify a fact or an emotion and compare it with other facts or emotions. Before the unique it is impotent. Every love-affair has something in common with every other love-affair, and there are lessons to be drawn of the meaning and metaphysical nature of love. Of them at another time.

But of that which is unique I cannot, and I do not greatly care, to write.

> God be praised, the meanest of his creatures
> Boasts two soul-sides, one to face the world with,
> One to show a woman when he loves her.

And that side I cannot analyse, even to myself, because one can analyse only by comparing, and the unique is incomparable. Even to attempt to analyse is necessarily to falsify, and here are memories which I do not care to falsify even to myself.

> Thus they see you, praise you, think they know you,
> Out of my own self, I dare to phrase it.
> But the best is when I glide from out them,
> Cross a step or two of dubious twilight,
> Come out on the other side, the novel
> Silent silver lights and darks undreamed of,
> Where I hush and bless myself with silence.

There remain some memories stamped for ever on the mind—Marjorie, like Furse's Diana, standing on top of a hill, two dogs on the leash and the wind blowing through her hair—the memory of her one night as she swept into the drawing-room before dinner at a large party—how proud I was!—her first murmur in the nursing-home as she came to after the anæsthetic of Christopher's birth, 'They say he's just like Peter.' It is enough. 'I bless myself with silence' where words would be impotent, and, if words there must be, I on the whole prefer quotation. That is what poets are for—or one of the things that poets are for—to give to the tongue-tied and the shy words which excuse them from the need of too detailed a description of their own emotions. For myself I say only 'Good-bye' and 'Thank you.'

I accepted with all shame the rebuke to my crude and flippant braggadocio, nor was it only my attitude to air raids that remorse caused me to re-examine. My whole political philosophy, unshaken by the lesson of David's loss, only perplexed when Bobby died at Dunkirk, then at last seemed to me to be insufficient. Up till the war I had been contented to be a crude and conventional Socialist Left-Winger, denouncing unearned increment and appeasement, calling for the end of privilege and the death of Fascism. The Battle of Britain did not bring to me any greater love of Fascism, and it still seemed to me, and still seems to me as I write these words, that the cry for the abolition of privilege was a cry aimed to satisfy a demand of real importance. But the sort of abolition of privilege envisaged in a Socialist's Act of Parliament was obviously grossly superficial and insufficient. You could abolish hereditary titles and privileges or abolish inherited wealth, if you wanted to, without much difficulty, but it is to play with words to pretend that a society in which privilege was thus abolished would of itself be an equalitarian society. Phrases about 'the career open to talent' mask the reality that certain talents for organising, certain gifts of rhetoric do enable some people to obtain inordinate power over their fellow-men—in all societies, but above all in societies which deny hereditary privilege. It is absurd to discuss democracy on its abstract merits by asking why one man should have more power than another. One must face the concrete question, In such a society as that of twentieth-century England into whose hands under democratic forms does power pass? When the question was posed thus I felt that there was no answer save that as a general rule it passed into the hands of the unbalanced.

Perhaps my nerves, exasperated by the contrast between the tragedy around and the fatuity of the clubs, betrayed me into too unqualified an answer. But, recollecting my emotion in comparative tranquillity, I cannot very much disapprove of it. There are, I know, exceptions—here and there a bustling under-secretary who carries in his head the name of the Government department to which he is attached. But the exceptions are rare. Democratic countries in recent years—whether England or America or the Latin countries—have as a general rule been governed by lunatics, and the rule of the lunatics continues until in refuge from it the nation plunges into totalitarianism or the rule of the maniacs. The progression from the one to the other is logical and inevitable, as Plato saw.

It was not, I came now to feel, purely an accident that the country happened to be ruled by such men. There was an inevitable quality in the Parliamentary life which drove men who practised it for long a little mad. Tony Arbuthnot was not any madder than the rest of us when he was at Eton. He was, if you like, while the possessor of other more attractive qualities, empty-headed, insolent, ignorant and cursed with the Etonian's curious conviction that, provided only that one possesses self-confidence, no other equipment is necessary not only to make one successful, but also to make one right. I remember very well how angry his tutor was at Cambridge when Tony one day committed himself in an essay to the generalisation, 'The Papacy from its first foundation has been invariably held by men of immoral and unworthy life.'

'How many Popes' names do you know?' asked his tutor.

'Oh, there was Alexander Borgia,' said Tony, 'and—and all the rest.'

'Do you happen to remember any of their names?' asked the Don with academic acidity.

'No, to tell the truth, I can't quite remember their names,' said Tony, unabashed, 'but, of course, I know their faces.'

On examination it was discovered that Tony had not the least idea when the Papacy was founded. I do not mean to say that he was not acquainted with the nice points of dispute between Roman Catholics and Anglo-Catholics about the Petrine claims. I mean that he had no idea what the Papacy purported to be.

'Is the Pope a Roman Catholic?' he asked, and was confident that St. Peter could not have been the first Pope because it did not say anything about it in the Bible.

'Some people think it does and some think it doesn't', explained his tutor, himself a pious Anglo-Catholic. 'It all depends upon one's interpretation of a certain rather famous passage.'

'Well, if the Dons can't make up their minds, how do you expect me to get it right?' asked Tony.

'Different views!' he said afterwards to me with every scorn. 'The old fool did not know what the verse meant himself.'

Yet that did not seem to me lunacy. It was just insolence, for it never occurred to him that it could for a second matter 'what these damned Dons say.' In the same way it was a great insolence that a man, so wholly ignorant of everything, should aspire to become a Member of Parliament and, so aspiring, should make no attempt to equip himself either intellectually or spiritually before becoming one. But, had he carried his natural insolence into political life, told his constituents the truth that he did not care a damn whether they were unemployed or not and retired after a brief bout of inglorious failure, he would not at any rate have been untrue to his character. What was happening during these months was more absurd by far.

While bombs dropped on Coventry and Plymouth, while frozen Greeks and Italians confronted one another in the Albanian snows, Tony was sitting on the committee of a ridiculous organisation called the Society for Rearranging the Poor. (On second thoughts, I do not believe that I have got the title quite right, but it was words to that effect and that was what he always called it—with characteristic cynicism—in his private conversation.) He had a ramshackle collection of colleagues on his committee. I went one day to give evidence before it—God knows why—but Tony said, 'You might as well give the evidence as anybody else.' It was, he said, 'as good as a play.'

There was a very old lord to preside over it—a nice old boy who liked to rearrange the poor in exactly the same way that he liked to rearrange the stamps in his stamp album—'for something to do' as he very sensibly confessed. He wanted everybody to be labelled with a ticket as a preliminary condition for the game of changing all the tickets, as he put it, 'of keeping the workers circulating.' Then there was a comedian, who, of course, like all comedians, was desperately anxious to prove that he was not just a funny man. He had tried preaching in churches on the League of Nations, but, as he had five wives living, he found it difficult to get engagements in churches that carried much publicity. So he joined the committee, and, joining it, solved the matrimonial problem by putting two of his ex-wives on it with him. One was a fading film-star, and God knows what the other was. When I say that I do not merely use the Deity as a euphemism for my own ignorance. It was not merely that I did not know the secrets of her soul and life. I knew her as well as anybody else did. But the secrets of that elusive character are best left to the knowledge of God alone. To seek to know would be like eating the apple of Eden. Then there were two other politicians besides Tony, and there was a novelist who had been taken up for a time by the smart set but was now anxious to prove that he was not really a gentleman. He was an embittered man, he confided to me, because twenty years ago he had written his masterpiece—an obituary ode in eulogy of the most distinguished of his colleagues, who at the time had pneumonia. But unfortunately the colleague recovered and survived and the masterpiece remained still unpublished. 'A rasping good ode it was,' he said sadly, 'but all so personal one couldn't make it apply to someone else.' There was a nice bishop who was always explaining that he was in great perplexity. There was a Don who made a lot of money by talking on the B.B.C. and who did really speak in private life and when there were no reporters present of 'We who lead the higher life.' He had a beard which went to and fro like one of those things that musicians use to beat time—a metronome, isn't it? Then there was a popular journalist who despised the novelist and who complained on the day that Paris fell, 'Nothing in the papers, I suppose, as usual'—meaning thereby that his signed article had been cut out.

Perhaps there were one or two more I have forgotten. Oh yes, there was a rather nice dirty man, who had recently become a Buddhist and seemed to find the profession of his faith almost a full-time occupation. He was, I believe, some sort of a secret Don, and from time to time would creep off to coach somebody in God knows what. Then there was, to do the committee justice, one man who was warden of some sort of settlement down in the East End. He really did see the poor from time to time, but he was, as far as I could gather, the only member who did.

It was all delightfully informal, and they paid no attention whatever to those who appeared before them to give evidence. I was ushered into their large room and waved cheerily by Tony to a chair. They were debating when I went in the payment of a pension to an employee who had been incapacitated in an air raid.

'Somebody or other,' the novelist was saying, 'once said that the poor we have always with us. I believe it was . . .'

'Jesus Christ,' put in the journalist, who knew everything.

'Ah, yes,' said the novelist. 'The name was just on the tip of my tongue.'

'Well, He told us to leave the poor to bury their own dead.'

'Where did He say that?' asked the bishop.

'Oh, I don't know where, I'm sure,' said the novelist. 'Somewhere abroad, I suppose.'

'Oh dear,' said the bishop.

'Now I take it,' said the novelist, ignoring the interruption, 'that that means that the compensation of the incapacitated is the State's business and that it would be very wrong for us to interfere in the matter.'

'I don't follow that at all,' protested the bishop. 'If we are going to base the argument on scriptural precedents, after all the Good Samaritan did not report the wounded man to an official of the Ministry of Social Security. He did what he could to help him himself.'

'There wasn't a Ministry of Social Security in those days,' put in the journalist, who knew everything.

'Oh, wasn't there?' said the film-star.

'It makes all the difference if there was not a Ministry of Social Security,' said the peer, from the top of the table.

'But there isn't yet,' said the bishop, 'and meanwhile we cannot just let the poor starve.'

The politicians could not imagine why not, so long as they really did starve and were not left just alive enough to vote Labour.

'Oh, well, you're a bishop. You believe in God, so you're biased,' they said.

'You're being asked to give the money, so I think that you might be called a little biased,' said the bishop.

'I think not,' said the politicians.

'We who lead the higher life,' said the comedian, mimicking the Don and pinching the right-hand buttock of one wife with his left hand, and the left-hand buttock of the other wife with his right hand, 'we who lead the higher life must not be forgetful of our responsibilities.'

A hush fell on the assembly.

'We must live in hope,' said the peer.

At that moment a bomb burst in the road outside. The bishop started to say grace, and all the rest of the committee vanished under the table. In the confusion they quite forgot to take my evidence, which mattered little, as I had none of any moment to give.

'But what's the point of it all?' I asked Tony afterwards.

'Oh, we work things out,' he answered, 'and one day something will come of it. One day there will be a thing called the Arbuthnot Act, which will say that anyone will go to jug who blows his nose on a Friday, and a lot of chaps will get jobs as inspectors to see that they don't, and chaps like you and me will get jobs as inspectors of inspectors to see that the inspectors inspect. You're quite wrong, I assure you, if you think that nothing ever gets done.'

'I didn't say that nothing got done,' I answered. 'I asked what was the point of it.'

'Oh, it would do one no good to get a name as a reactionary,' said Tony. 'Forward-looking Conservatism—Tory democracy—bold, sweeping social reforms—that's the game these days. The wise guys among the Labour people, of course, are all saying how patriotic and conservative they are and how they are really quite open-minded whether anything ought to be nationalised or not. But if you're a Conservative then you must do the Left-Wing stunt. The way to get on is to be broad-minded, and being broad-minded means belonging to one party and preaching the principles of the other. There was a chap in history called Sir Robert Peel who found that out.'

The unsophisticated may think that, because there was a party truce and a Coalition Government, there were therefore no party politics during these years. It is far from so.

Politics were not improved by being removed from the comparatively clean atmosphere of Eatanswill. At the contested election the people have at any rate the illusion of choice between Tweedledum and Tweedledee. Under a party truce the fight is the secret fight for the nomination behind the committee-room's locked door, and there need be no check of shame on the selection of a candidate who is inevitably to be returned unopposed or at least not seriously opposed.

I remember once by some strange chance hearing Tony address a meeting of his constituents.

'After this war,' he told them, 'we are going to build a new and a cleaner world—a world worthy of those splendid lads who gave their all so that we might live. We—all of us—you and I—we must see to it that we do not allow that world to be wrecked and ruined by selfishness and greed. We are not going back to the old, bad ways again; we are going forward to the new, good ways—to the world of the vision and to the City Beautiful. "I will not cease from mental strife,"' he cried, lifting his eyes up piously to his third wife—a very decent little chorus-girl, who was grinning down at him from the gallery and who gave a friendly wave of her hand.

> "Nor shall my sword sleep in my hand,
> Till we have built Jerusalem
> In England's green and pleasant land."

'Got that?' he said to the reporters afterwards. It was a most extraordinary performance.

After the meeting Tony and I drove back to his club. A Minister had died that morning. It meant a reshuffle in the Cabinet; it meant everybody moving up one all along the line; it meant a bye-election. The politicians crowded round the bar. Tony called for a double brandy.

'They'd never give it to Bertie.'

'The Tories have made a condition that, whatever happens, they will always have the Exchequer.'

'At the Bank they say they'd as soon have a Socialist. They never had any Conservative who ate out of their hand the way Snowden did.'

'Yes, so much that in the end he ceased to be a Socialist.'

'Hang it all, everyone's allowed to cross the floor once in his life. That's one of the rules.'

'Well, if Bertie does get it, that means that they've got to bring in somebody else at the India Office, and if there's a Labour under-secretary there, then they'll want a Conservative under-secretary at the Dominions, and, with his father-in-law's pull and his mother's money, I should think that Jimmy stands a very good chance. So no wonder he thinks it a very good job that both he and his father married after all.'

'They say you have to pay back your salary and put down £500 a year for that seat.'

'Well, naturally. It's as safe as a house even when there is a war on.'

'Do you think they would ever stand for a Jew down there?'

'Of course they would, provided he paid £700 instead of £500, and Jimmy would be willing for that.'

'Why don't you stand?' said a man next to me.

'Well, primarily because I'm not a Conservative. I'm a Socialist.'

'A Socialist, are you?' said another man. 'That's just what I want. The present Socialist candidate's a miserable little pipsqueak of a railwayman, and they think that they can beat him with anyone. So they're giving the Conservative nomination to a local manufacturer. But if you get the Socialist nomination, then I can say that you're the hell of a good speaker and that it takes a Londoner to beat a Londoner. So they'll have to give me the Conservative nomination. Do put up, won't you? Be a sport. I'll stand you a drink.'

I refused to be tempted even thus. He turned to other topics and all evaporated, as is the way with politics, in an orgy of wishful drinking.

'But what is the point of it all?' I repeated to Tony when we had come away.

'Well, in peace-time,' he said, 'one gets a hell of a lot of free meals—I mean really free meals—the sort where one does not have to ask anybody back.'

How strange is the contrast between the majestic metaphysics of the State and the extraordinary creatures who actually run it! The mountain has laboured and has given birth to a whole litter of mice, each one more ridiculous than the last.

V

I WENT to Ruth the subsequent week-end to help with the hay-making. Ruth herself in her enormous-brimmed Mexican hat forking up, Billy Perkins on the cart receiving, working on with monotony through the whole long June day, with that patient, regular rhythm which enables the good workman to go on for ever—from time to time peeling one of his innumerable waistcoats to reveal yet another waistcoat beneath, the horses, Dot and Carry, blinking in the shafts. One could not but feel a contrast between this atmosphere and that of the clubs where 'men sit and hear each other groan.' One could not but feel that here was a picture of men doing right and there a picture of men doing wrong—I do not mean so much of men sinning in any particular word or act as of men living a life the whole form of which was different from that for which they were created.

Tired, I came home in the evening, and after dinner I picked out of the bookcase what I knew to be a favourite book of Bobby's—old Sir Thomas Overbury's *Character of a Yeoman.* I do not think that anybody had touched it since his death, and the marker was still in its place. It opened at the words:

> 'Though he be master, he says not to his servant, "Go to field" but "Let us go," and with his own eye doth both fatten his flock and set forward all manner of husbandry.'

Did the secret lie there? Was the great contrast between the right and the wrong life to be found in what Dante called courtesy? We Socialist politicians had been preaching the abolition of privilege and a classless society. But in practice we had not succeeded in abolishing class and privilege, but only in making everybody intolerably conscious of his class and the unprivileged intolerably conscious of their lack of privilege. And was this because class was inevitable in the nature of things and its abolition impossible? If so, was not perhaps Bobby's way, and I think that I might say Billy Perkins' way, the right way—the frank acceptance of class divisions as a fact, the full understanding that the first demand of honour was that one should not selfishly abuse one's privileges but should use them for the service of others? Bobby used to argue that class distinctions were a reality but not an ultimate reality. Men must and did have privileges over one another in social and political and economic arrangements. It was not so much that that was the best way of ordering things; it was the only way. You could profess that you would abolish privilege, but in practice you could only abolish old privileges by substituting new privileges. But what rendered privilege tolerable was that it should be exercised against a background of understanding of its relative unimportance. Men, unequal in the details of their income and in their political authority, were equal in far more important matters. I remembered how Tony had once suggested to Bobby that he was a better man than Billy Perkins, his cowman, and I remembered Bobby's honest amazement at the novelty and absurdity of the suggestion.

The reason why politicians tended to go mad, Bobby used to argue, was that a man ought to live his full life as a human being and then contribute of his experience in that life to the nation's political wisdom. So, too, with writers. The notion that a man should be a politician and nothing but a politician, or a writer and nothing but a writer, and consciously use life only to provide him with the matter for his trade, was to his mind a fantastic notion. Its indulgence made men bad politicians and bad writers. It degraded them to a sub-human form. The nation's affairs, he would argue, must in practice, whatever theory might preach, be managed by those who were brought up in the tradition, in which politics were but one of the interests of a man of culture, or they would be managed very badly. It was no accident that democracy's two great leaders, the two rocks of sanity in a world of madness, Roosevelt and Churchill, should have been men who owed their position, among other things, to a privilege of birth, the last of the patricians.

I was not as yet quite prepared to follow Bobby in his farthest excursions into Dantesque eschatology nor into his unqualified championship of a governing class. But I did feel very strongly that he was right in his contention that political power should not be in the hands of men whose predominant interest was in politics. If everything was to be run by the State, as I, as a good Socialist, had hitherto argued, then it was indeed pertinent to ask what the statesmen were like. It meant being run by Tony Arbuthnot and his drinking pals. It meant Billy Perkins being ordered about by Tony Arbuthnot. I had never envisaged it in such concrete, personal terms before, but I could see now that it was necessary to envisage it thus. Ruth corroborated my fears. She told of a lady in the village who was to have a fifth child. Her nursemaid went to appeal for exemption from calling-up until the child had arrived. The tribunal inquired into the circumstances, and, having learnt them, the chairman said to the young girl, 'Mrs. Johnson should be ashamed of herself having five children in war-time. She ought to know better.'

'It would be bad enough at the best of times,' said Ruth 'that jacks-in-office should lay down the law about private matters like that. It would be bad enough if they talked sense, but when they talk arrant nonsense, discouraging families at the very time when larger families are our one possible hope of survival, it is past all bearing. The trouble with you Socialists is that, whenever you find something that is imperfectly done by private people, you make the assumption that it would be perfectly done if only it were done by the State. Now you're seeing who the State is, and I wish you joy of it.'

I remembered Bobby's account of his visit to the Governor of one of the Middle Western States in America. He was a cultured man. It was half-past eleven in the morning and the poor fellow was very drunk, with an empty whiskey bottle on the desk before him. 'L'état, c'est moi,' he said, holding out to Bobby a shaking hand, and closed his eyes and went to sleep. Therein lay a parable.

But what exactly was the solution? A new political programme to replace the old, inadequate political programme was not the solution. For it was the obsession with politics, not the obsession with any particular politics, which was the evil. I was prepared by now to confess myself a convert to Bobby's view that it was essential that political power should be in the hands of those to whom politics were only of subordinate interest. But in what should men be interested? It clearly was not sufficient that our would-be politicians should equip themselves with a dilettante interest in culture and know a 'decent' picture when they saw it. Something more was required. But what more? I was not yet clear of the answer.

As I have already said, at the outbreak of the war I was a more or less conventional, anti-appeasement left-winger in politics, believing in democracy, the abolition of privilege and opposition to Fascism, and believing that all these things were important. Religion I did not believe to be either true or important. I did not think that clergymen had anything important to say or that their messages were in any way relevant to the world's troubles. If I was not strongly anti-clerical, that was only because I hardly ever came across clergymen. Their influence both in private and public conduct was, I thought, negligible, and there was therefore no sense in wasting energy in battling against what was unimportant. But, had the clergy been at all strong or in any way interfered with my life, I should certainly have been rabidly anti-clerical. I thought that the solutions were political, economic and secularist.

Now the war did not convert me from my old to any new political faith. I felt no temptation to abandon Socialism in order to become a Fascist or to become a Conservative. I still believed what I had believed before—that men should be equal and that privilege should be abolished—but, when Socialists came into power, I saw that there were many more forms of privilege and inequality than I had previously understood and that some of those forms flourished just as vigorously under democratic as under reactionary governments. It was a very striking trait in Robert Fossett's character that he always listened with perfect courtesy to the address of anyone however humble or unkempt, that he never in the least resented any frankness of speech simply because of the speaker's poverty. To have perverted justice in a decision because of the wealth of one of the parties would have been to him an unthinkable wickedness. Now Bobby had no sort of belief in an equality of income. The notion seemed to him nonsensical. But he had a very fundamental belief in the ultimate equality of man.

I would not for a moment say that all country squires had such a belief. Indeed, it is very arguable that very few rich men can preserve that faith in spite of their riches. Nor would I say that no Liberals have such a true liberal faith. But I would say that this belief in fundamental equality is comparatively irrelevant to what I now came to think of as man's superficial political profession. It could be found as commonly absent or as commonly present in men of every political party. There are innumerable forms of contempt for equality and ample opportunity to combine that contempt, if a man wishes to combine it, with any political faith. You may, if you care to do so, think the more of a man because of his birth or his wealth. But it is every bit as great a violence to the equalitarian faith to think more of him because he has a gift of repartee, a talent for intrigue, a quick brain, a dash of impudence, a trick of words, a good digestion or any of the other qualities that are needed for success. It was a crudity of the old capitalism that a man's worth was assessed entirely by his capacity for making money. But after a little experience of them one trembles even to think what are the qualities which are allowed to bring success in the new civilisations, where money-making is no longer permitted.

In this sad summer of our finest hour, the contrast between the Battle of Dunkirk and the Battle of Whitehall—the bureaucrat filling the unforgiving minute, the political jostling and intriguing for place—was not inspiring. The easiest road was one of reaction from the first high hopes into despair, into the *sæva indignatio* of a Swift, into saying that all forms of government must be managed by men and that man, armed with power, was incorrigible. I had friends—Robert Fossett and others—fighting out on the beaches of Dunkirk. I was myself then at the War Office. One day I received the news that Fossett and a couple more of my best friends had been killed, and, going to the office, I found myself embroiled there in one of those cases of peculiarly wooden selfishness with which Whitehall is so familiar. I murmured to myself the lines from the 'Ancient Mariner':

> The many men so beautiful
> And they all dead did lie,
> And a thousand, thousand slimy things
> Lived on, and so did I.

What could it matter, since all was hopeless and all was irretrievable? For forms of government let fools indeed contest, since fools, it seemed, were in any event destined to administer them.

A cynic is sometimes a good physician of despair. I had a conversation with Tony a few days later at the club—the same conversation, I think, as that mentioned in the opening page of this book. I developed my thesis of despair.

'Well, that's not very helpful, is it?' said Tony.

'I do not know that there is any point in being helpful, when there is no hope anyway,' I said. 'After all, *Eloi, Eloi, lama sabachthani* was not exactly a helpful remark.'

'What on earth are you talking about?' asked Tony, who had never read anything.

He stubbed out a cigarette in the ashtray.

'In any event,' he said, 'it's all rot what you say. Things over here are admittedly a pretty fair racket. But still, England's a good deal better than Germany.'

This was certainly true. I did not waver in my belief that

England, for all her faults, was a healthier country than Nazi Germany, or for that matter than France of the Front Populaire or indeed than many other foreign countries. And such an admission at least forbade despair by its admission that, as in the circles of Dante's Hell, there were degrees of badness. It proved something. But what exactly did it prove? Did it prove that English political life was better than that of other countries? Or did it rather, as I half suspected, prove that English life was better than that of other countries precisely because so much of it was kept out of the clutch of the politicians? If so, then we had an admirable right to fight totalitarianism, though it was a strange paradox that we should apparently be accepting the totalitarian philosophy at the very moment of our triumph over it.

Bobby Fossett used to argue that political power ought to be in the hands of men of some hereditary position and some inherited culture, because it was only tolerable that power should be wielded by those to whom the wielding of it was not a preoccupation. No man should ever be appointed to office unless he was both spiritually and financially prepared to resign from it if necessary. Naturally, from my point of view, I thought that Bobby a little exaggerated the need for hereditary position and wealth to ensure an independent mind. One can inherit brainlessness just as much as one can inherit brain. Yet there is no doubt of the general truth that political life, if it is going to be tolerable, must not be a preoccupation. England is superior to Germany precisely because England still has some politicians of this ampler culture. There are, it is true, many English politicians who have no such culture. I do not know that these men in themselves are particularly better than French or German politicians, but fortunately, for the present at any rate, counterbalanced by their betters, they have less power.

'Yes,' Tony broke in, 'but what are these other things besides politics in which they are to be interested? Horse racing?'

That was the conundrum with which he left me. It solved itself for me, in so far as it was solved, as follows.

Dons should be great eccentrics—shuffling, wheezy, short-sighted, unpunctual, peering old men, losing railway tickets in old manuscripts that were made before the birth of time, never travelling by train save when they have forgotten to wash off one cheek's shaving-soap, drinking enormously but with heads like rocks, quarrelling about digammas and the circulation of the port, contemptuous of undergraduates, derisive of politicians, nursing, it may be, some secret private doubts of Christianity, sufficient to prevent them from practice of their religion but loudest to jeer at those who aired their doubts in a public press.

When I was up at Oxford just after the last war we had among us a game of collecting strange Dons. There were a few Dons who were for ever consorting with undergraduates, asking them to their rooms, even visiting their clubs. Such Dons we despised. But on the other hand there were the nobler Dons, masters of useless and esoteric subjects, who were careful to have no pupils and fewer friends, who lived at the tops of high towers up interminable staircases, where they drank alone behind thickly sported oaks, only emerging occasionally in gathering dusk to insult their colleagues. Such Dons one was proud to collect, and the capture of one yet dimmer and odder than those hitherto known was generally accepted as a feather in a cap. All collecting has about it something morbid, and the collecting of Dons was doubtless of the nature of a vice, though it was a vice that in contrast with many of those in which undergraduates indulged was comparatively natural.

In any event, it had been my greatest triumph in this game to have collected the Reader in Javanese. I had collected him by the unsubtle technique of going into his room to be sick, mistaking it for another, one evening when I was drunk. His reactions to this manœuvre were at first adverse, but on reflection, unlike Queen Victoria, he was amused. Though he had been Reader in Javanese for forty-three years, he had never yet had a pupil, and I do not think that he had ever before met an undergraduate. He suggested that we should go out together into the street to look for the tram-lines. I, being, as I say, drunk, had quite forgotten that the tram-lines had been taken up seven years before, when Mr. Morris (afterwards Lord Nuffield) had driven the horse-trams off the street. The Reader in Javanese was, I imagine, well aware of this and made the suggestion only because he preferred that I should be sick where the tram-lines used to be rather than on his carpet, or it may be—I never knew—that he had not been out in the streets for the last seven years and really thought that the horse-trams still ran there.

In any event the suggestion seemed to me an admirable one, and we sallied out and, while with the aid of a torch we searched together for the tram-lines, he told me how he had once been an Anglican clergyman, but had been unfrocked for what he called 'immoraality'—he pronounced the 'a' long. 'It was not,' he said, 'what you or I would call immoraality. I was only living with a black woman.' I was touched by his assumption of my enlightened agreement on the point of morals, and indeed to the somewhat callow free-thinking and free-living of omniscient twenty-one I was troubled, not by his approval of cohabitation with a black woman, but only by the implication that there might have been something wrong had he been living with a white one. However, I solved it, as one always did solve all puzzling intellectual problems at that time, by asking him to lunch..

My conquest was generously hailed as tremendous. He

was a yellow admiral. He was a three-cornered Cape of Good Hope, and out of mere self-respect I had in a measure to maintain this friendship thus strangely formed. I did so throughout the rest of my disreputable Oxford career, and, oddly enough, even afterwards. I used to see the old boy every now and again when he came to London. The friendship was maintained, on his part, for the most sensible and intelligible of reasons. I was the only person in England who stood him a free lunch, and therefore, obedient to Polonius' advice, he grappled me to his soul with hoops of steel. 'Steel' was the word. Quite why I persisted in this strange obstinacy of hospitality I never knew. One enjoyed at first the attraction of the company of complete ignorance —discovered that he had never heard of Bernard Shaw and did not know the name of the Prime Minister or the horse that won the Cesarewitch or the Dean's wife. But this was after all a comparatively negative pleasure or foundation for a reputation. The truth was that he did not know what everybody else knew, but he did not know anything else either. He was an ignoramus, a bore, and almost a natural. He was one of those strange beings who can talk after a fashion innumerable languages—almost every language, in fact, except English, which he spoke like a German, and, I had reason to believe, Javanese. Nothing is worse for the brain than linguistic accomplishment, and, like most Mezzofantis, he was an idiot in all his languages. Whether he knew any Javanese or not I could not, of course, say, but I do not suppose for a moment that he knew a word of it. He said that he knew it well, but I never caught him out telling the truth about anything else, so I do not suppose that he told the truth about that.

With the coming of the war he got a job in the Ministry of Information. As his handwriting was not at all clear, they thought that he was the Reader in Japanese and so put him into the Korean department. There he sat in a room along with a magician who had been expelled from Sicily, and they copied great lists of the statistics of the exports from Korea to Formosa out of the *Encyclopædia Britannica.* The encyclopædias were always getting mixed up with bits of dried goat-skin that the magician left lying about on the table, and they sometimes rubbed out the chalk-marks that he had made all over the floor. So, what with one thing and another, there was usually a row and the statistics were always copied out wrong. But, as nobody in any event ever used them and as they were all anyway printed quite right in the *Encyclopædia Britannica,* that did not matter in the least.

Then the Minister of Information heard that some of the Japanese were Shintoists by religion and worshipped their ancestors. He thought that it would be a good thing that a clergyman who was the son of a peer should be put into the department to sit alongside the Reader in Javanese and the magician. There were, it seemed, only two such clergymen available, and one of them was ruled out because he had supported General Franco in the Spanish Civil War. So George Borthwick, being the other one, got the job.

George Borthwick had been captain of m'tutor's at Eton the half before Bobby Fossett. He was then a haughty and grim Olympian, I a grubby, inky fag in Middle Fourth, and such acquaintanceship as we formed was only acquaintanceship in the most wholly formal and unpleasant of senses. After the last war, in which he lost a leg, he had got ordained and gone out to New Zealand. Therefore, what with one thing and another, I had never seen very much of him, even though I had always heard a good deal of him from Bobby Fossett, who until death kept up a constant correspondence with him and had a high opinion of his abilities. He was now a Canon Residentiary of Ripon.

I used sometimes to drop in at the Ministry of Information in order to see the Reader in Javanese, and it was thus that to my joy I met again George Borthwick. I never keep up with old schoolfellows; to do so seems to me almost a form of cheating. But I am always delighted when I meet one by chance, looking at the meeting as a windfall from Providence. I hastily book up lunch and drinks to celebrate the occasion. So now with George, and hence it came about that we had lunch together a few days later. I produced to him what was then my King Charles' head about the fatuities of the politicians, but, whereas this tirade aroused most people to excited argument, it only produced in George a bored agreement as to a platitude.

'Of course,' he said.

'Of course?' I replied. 'But then, if of course, so what?'

'How can I say what?' he asked. 'You have tried to answer a question before you have asked it. How can I tell what you are driving at?'

'Meaning precisely?' I asked.

'Well, you say that politicians are no good and that Bobby Fossett was a good fellow and that problems can be solved and problems cannot be solved, but what do you mean by good? What is your view of the nature of things and of the end of Man?'

'Good God,' I said, 'it might be Socrates.'

'Perhaps,' he said, 'but is not a possible answer to your complaint that there is no solution the answer that to expect problems to be solved in that final sort of way is itself the disease from which you are suffering? You invent the belief, in defiance of all evidence, that Man is naturally good and then, when things go wrong, as they always do, instead of putting the blame on everybody and on the Nature of Man, you invent again some scapegoat man or scapegoat nation or scapegoat class and pretend that it alone is the villain and must be eliminated and then all will be well—and of course it isn't. If you mean by saying that things are hopeless, that there is little chance that the day after Hitler is scuppered the sun will rise upon a rosy dawn of perfect peace, of course things are fortunately quite hopeless.'

'I suppose that it's all caused by human selfishness,' I said.

'Oh, that's a bit superficial,' he said. 'People have always been pretty selfish, but the calamities of our time are quite exceptional. There must be a further and more particular cause than that. Is life meant to be like that at all? You remember King Alfred's vision of Our Lady in the Ballad of the White Horse.'

'Of course I don't, George,' I said. 'Don't be such an idiot. You know very well that I don't remember anything.'

'Well, he met Our Lady,' said George, 'at a time when the war was going for him as badly as it could, and she said to him:

> I tell you naught for your comfort
> Yea, naught for your desire.
> Save that the sky grows darker yet
> And the sea rises higher.

Now, King Alfred thought that that was good news.'

'Why did he?' I said, by now thoroughly bewildered.

'Because he was a Christian,' said George, 'and to the Christian life is of its nature a warfare, a conflict between powers of good and powers of evil at issue in the world and in the individual soul.'

'Thursday next week,' I said. 'Lunch with me Thursday next week. I must go now. I really must, George. Thank you so much. It has been so nice seeing you.'

I am like that. I hate being rushed in my mind. I have in some ways a tolerably good mind, but I have also, I am well aware, a slow mind. If a novel idea is thrown at me by one familiar with it or by one with a quicker mind than mine, I am at a disadvantage. So I refuse to accept it merely because I cannot immediately see the answer to it. I postpone answering until I have had time to think it out alone.

From this luncheon followed other luncheons and other conversations with George throughout the summer. I will not weary the reader with the whole story of what I suppose that I may call my course of instruction. I certainly learnt many lessons that were greatly to my benefit. In the first place, it did me a world of good to be shown my manifest intellectual inferiority. I had thought in my ignorance of all clergymen as simple-minded and imbecile. I found George far better read and far quicker-witted than I. I had but to go to his study and to look at the backs of the books that lined his shelves to be ashamed of the airy impudence with which I had hitherto dismissed Christianity. Like so many other moderns, I had carelessly dismissed it without ever bothering to inquire the names, let alone the arguments, of better men than I who had given their lives to the refutation of my doubts. I had even had the impudence to sink from agnosticism to despair, ignorant alike of that which I did not know and that in which I had lost hope.

George had a ready habit of twisting up some new facet of truth as he saw it out of even the most unpromising remarks. I could never tell of any weapon that I brought that it would not be wrested from me and assumed into his hands.

'Catholicism's a buffoon's religion,' I remember that I said one day. 'All the chaps that write funny columns in the papers are Roman Catholics.'

'That seems to me a very good argument in favour of Roman Catholicism,' said George. 'No one is more boring than the man who is always explaining how much smarter he is than everyone else and how he scores off everybody else and how no one can ever get the better of him. An egoist can never be a funny man because no one is interested in the person who is only interested in himself. Humility, I would say, is the requisite for humour, and humility is after all the most fundamental of all the Christian virtues.'

'But a lot of humble people are very boring,' I said.

'Oh, I don't say,' he replied, 'that all humble people are funny, but I do say that all funny people are humble, and, if all funny people are also Roman Catholics, that is a very good point for them. But personally I don't believe that all Roman Catholics do write paragraphs for the funny papers.'

'Oh yes, they do,' I said, 'because they can't get serious jobs.'

'That's a great piece of luck for them,' said George.

'They don't think so,' I said. 'They are always complaining about it. Michael Paravane never stops complaining.'

'In this unbelieving modern world,' said George, 'the funny men are the only people that the British public will take seriously. They have a curious prestige of irrelevance.'

'Yes,' I agreed, 'I had a conference of brigadiers eating out of my hand the other day when they discovered that I knew Wyndham Lewis. They thought if I knew that I must know everything.'

'Any politician could sweep the country,' said George, 'if only he would say that his programme was not his own but that of Nat Gubbins' cat.'

George's fundamental proposition was that, whether Christianity was true or not, it was at the least important. Nothing could be more important than to learn all that we can learn about a future life—to decide whether we must reject the possibility, whether we must be agnostic, or whether we can confidently look forward to life everlasting. It is obviously absurd to argue *in vacuo* whether Christians or secularists are good men, because the whole notion of what is good is coloured by acceptance or rejection of

Christianity. So far George seemed to me quite obviously right. And he was perhaps even more fully justified in his contempt for the slightly more sophisticated secularists of the type that write for the weekly papers and even sometimes proclaim themselves as agnostics in print. Their lack of reading and the impudence of rejecting on such slender examination what for two thousand years mankind had held as its highest possession were alike amazing. 'Peter,' George once said to me, after I had been giving him a lecture on Sir James Frazer's *Golden Bough*, imagining that those pages contained a final refutation of Christian claims, 'you should read some books.' It was a rebuke which I and others alike deserved.

In contrast with the dullness of the secularist world from which I came I was enormously impressed with George's confidence in reason, with his rare power to distinguish between what was wished and what was proved, with his willingness to carry the argument through. It did not need many talks to convince me that, as between Christianity, when it found a competent expositor, and what is impudently known as modern thought the victory lay completely with Christianity. This had only been masked from me hitherto because so many of the pretended champions of Christianity had allowed themselves to be blackmailed by the bludgeonings of the secularists into fighting with the secularists' weapon of sentimentality. There was a coherence in the Christian view of life which was lacking in those of its opponents.

At the same time I was not yet quite a convert. George's appeal was to reason, and it was therefore of no use to ask with Bishop Blougram, 'Has it your vote to be so if it can?' The question was 'Was it proved to be so?' And, for all its attractive logical form, for all its superiority over its rivals, there were, I felt, a few important lacunæ in George's case which still remained quite unbridged. I jotted them down one night on a piece of paper after I had got home from a long and wrestling argument with him. The next day I presented them to him, all solemnly typed out and headlined. Here they are:

VI

THE CASE AGAINST GEORGE

1. George's argument that because he exists and he did not make himself, therefore God must exist to have made him seems to me a good one. He sets out all the traditional Thomist proofs, and they all seem to me sensible, except that Kant is obviously quite right in saying that the argument from design at the best proves an Architect rather than a Creator. But my real difficulty begins when one reverses the argument. It may be that we cannot explain George's existence except by positing God's existence. But let us start from God's existence. If God existed, absolute and self-sufficient Being, what conceivable motive could He have had for creating George or the universe or any other lesser existence? 'So what?' says George. 'I admit that the fact of creation is a mystery. But it is a fact. Here we are. You do not annihilate us by saying that you cannot quite understand why we are here.' But it is my suspicion that there may be quite another explanation. Kant may be right in saying that the conception of causality only holds at all within the world of experience and that it is therefore quite illegitimate to use it in arguments concerning the ultimate nature of things.

2. Similarly, when all is said and done, none of the explanations either of the existence of evil or of the existence of freedom really explains either of them. Here again, says George, are mysteries. But when other people contradict

themselves George calls it a contradiction; when he contradicts himself he calls it a mystery. I dare say that Dr. Johnson has said about as much about freedom as any man can say: 'All argument is against it; all experience is for it.' But people don't seem altogether to understand the consequence of that devastating judgment. If there are some places in human history where unreason takes the control from reason, then it is no longer certain how far we are justified in trusting reason as our guide at all, no longer certain where it is operative and where it is inoperative. So, too, with evil. Had it been really true, as Socrates taught, that *oudeis hekon hamartanei,* it would have been comparatively easy, but once we admit the possibility that a man should know the better and do the worse—

> Video meliora proboque; deteriora sequor—

then we are in the presence of unreason. Reason is not wholly monarch, and, if reason does not always rule, what is the faculty beyond reason which decides when reason applies and when it does not?

3. When George comes on to the explicitly Christian claims, I find a similar difficulty. George had no difficulty at all in turning inside out the airy easy rationalisers of the Christian story or of Christian history. It was not difficult to show the folly of those who said that Christ was not God but was a very good man. There were many of His sayings which, if He was only a man, were necessarily the words of a lunatic. So, too, it was easy and legitimate to turn on those who rejected the Resurrection and ask them what then they thought did happen on Easter Sunday morning. I think that he made out his case very well that all other explanations of the Christian origins or of early Christian history except the Christian explanation break down. But what do these negatives establish? I am certain that something utterly extraordinary happened on that first Easter

morning. I am inclined to think it probable that Christ rose again from the dead, and, if so, I do not dispute that His Resurrection was one of the most remarkable events in human history. But that is just the trouble. I think that it was one of the most remarkable events in human history. The Christian thinks that it was the most remarkable event. I would agree that the miracle of a resurrection from the dead would prove almost anything—would prove anything in the world except only what it was claimed to prove. Suppose that Christ had said, 'I am the especial prophet of God, and, to prove it, after I have been crucified, God will raise me again from the dead,' then I should agree that He had amply proved His claim if only He succeeded in rising again. But when He says, 'I created the universe, and, to prove it, I will rise again,' I do not know that He does prove it, for I do not see how the great miracle, great as it may be, can prove the greater miracle.

'But how do you account for the Resurrection, then?' asked George.

'I don't account for it,' I said. 'I am inclined to believe it. But, if it happened, then it was something so wholly beyond my comprehension that I cannot even begin to guess what it means.'

'But what, then, do you think would prove the Divinity of Christ?' George persisted.

'It's not I that's saying that anything would prove it,' I answered. 'You might as well ask me what evidence I would accept to prove that twice two was five. Quite frankly to me it's not so much a question of accepting or rejecting the Athanasian definitions, but of attaching any meaning to them. How can Christ have been begotten—a verb in the past tense—and yet not begotten in time? It seems to me, I repeat, not so much a mystery as a contradiction.'

4. My fourth objection was what I can only call the old-

fashioned modernist objection to Hell. I just cannot believe in Hell. I can say that I believe in Hell, if you like, but I cannot really believe it in anything like the traditional orthodox sense, and—what is more—I do not believe that anyone else can. A lot of people think that they can just drop out Hell and go on believing all the rest. To them George answers that nothing is more false than the belief that Christ preached a gospel of unmitigated kindness and that afterwards wicked priests came along and invented Hell. On the contrary, Christ hurled at evil-doers the most appalling threats, and the Church has only taught the doctrine of Hell because she has been compelled to do so by Christ's utterly explicit words. That seems to me a perfectly valid answer of George's, but the answer creates a difficulty far greater than that which it solves. It is precisely the contradiction between the metaphysical claim that God is Love and the awful physical threats which Christ uttered which makes it impossible for me to accept His divinity. It is the New Testament which creates for me the difficulty of accepting the New Testament. It seems to me in the last analysis to stand self-condemned by its own self-contradiction.

'We would be just like Bishop Blougram and Gigadibs if only you gave me a little more to drink,' I said, as George finished reading my effusion, for these tussles were indeed rather exhausting.

'And if only you were a literary man,' said George.

'That's rather rude, isn't it?' I said.

'Well, I don't know if it was particularly polite to compare me to Bishop Blougram,' said George.

'Oh yes, it was,' I said. 'It was intended entirely as a compliment. I think that Blougram was a first-rate arguer and he followed the argument right through without sentimentality, just as you do.'

Anyway, there the matter stood between George and me and my scepticism and my scepticism of scepticism up till the end of the London blitz and my wife's death in it. As I have said, somehow I never considered the possibility that a bomb would fall either on me or mine. I prepared a shelter because the maids wanted one, but I would not go to it myself.

'I don't know why, but I hate sleeping in company,' I said to Tony. 'I can't bear the idea of going down there with the cook and the housemaid.'

'In these days,' said Tony, 'it's hard enough to get a cook. It's time enough to make up your mind whether you will sleep with her when you've got her.'

The reality of loss recalled me from this folly of flippancy. Of that loss I have already spoken as much as I care to speak. I am concerned at the moment with its effect on my metaphysics. 'Emotion,' Wordsworth told us, must be 'recollected in tranquillity' if it was to be the stuff of poetry. Such tranquillity—the tranquillity perhaps of sorrow—is also necessary for metaphysical analysis. As long as Marjorie was alive I do not know that I ever very deeply meditated on the meaning of being in love. In those first weeks of loss I found the whole problem for the first time pressing itself on my mind.

Is there such a thing as love? And, if so, what is it?

Let me make clear just what it is that I mean, for, considering how much people think and talk about love, it is extraordinary how little they speculate about its nature. Sex we know. But is being in love merely a very strong physical attraction? Or is there in it some other element beyond the physical? 'Our souls were in our names.' Is that just a piece of poet's rhetoric? Or has it a hard and real meaning? One can but answer from experience, but the volume of human experience is considerable, and it says that, over and beyond any physical satisfaction, love demands an identification of the will with that of the beloved. 'Not My Will, but Thine, be done' is its supreme expression.

I think that I can fairly say that I learnt all this through my own experience, and learnt it, as such a man as I almost always must learn, in suffering. But, in so far as I had another master, that master was Dante. I have never been able to understand the common approach to literature today. I can well understand the illiterate man, who has many compensating advantages for his inability to read. I can understand also the man who, though not illiterate, is yet not at all literary—who learns the secrets of things through some other medium than that of the written word. But I have never since my schooldays been able to understand the people who read great literature but never apparently try to learn from it—the pedants who search it only for its grammatical eccentricities, or the literary critics who pass their weekly verdicts upon it and then stagger out to the bar and the banausic world with the ink still wet upon the paper. Why one who has taken the trouble to learn to read should then waste that trouble upon reading books only of his own day I never could guess.

Bobby Fossett was a very good, if a very rare, example of the opposite—of a man who, while not an enormous reader, yet read mainly of the great central men and made those whom he had read the real masters of his life. Homer was, I suppose, his greatest hero, and a very fine hero doubtless to choose. There was a simplicity, a hatred of weariness, a love of the open air and the sweep of life about Bobby that made Homer a very natural love to him. But my own tastes run more to close arguing, and I do not think that there was ever a time, since my taste was formed at all, that Dante was not my favourite poet. I remember very well my first introduction to him. I was a History Specialist at Eton at the time, and our division used to meet at the back of

Warre Schools, those schools on the right in Common Lane, half-way down to the Fives Courts. It was a long winter evening—the school from five to quarter to six with the light blinking out on to a foggy November twilight and everybody longing for his tea. Bumble Jodson was taking us, and he was a man who found it very difficult to get through a History Schools, because he was too intelligent to think that there was any sense in dictating as notes matter that could perfectly well be found in the books already, and too lazy to invent things that could not be found there. So he used to fill in the times by all sorts of strange devices. We read *Alice in Wonderland,* and we gave one another lectures on the processes of spinning and weaving. We composed nonsense verses. We drew imaginary pictures of the Kings of Israel and Judah, and among other things we read for a few afternoons little snippets out of the *Divine Comedy* of Dante.

That was my first acquaintance with Dante—at the age of, I suppose, seventeen and a half. I cannot pretend that I then mastered his argument. Indeed, I cannot honestly pretend that I at that time grasped that he had an argument at all. I thought rather that in sublime prejudice he said that all the people that he liked were in Heaven and all the people that he disliked were in Hell, and then made up for them such adventures as occurred to him. Heaven was boring, but Hell I enjoyed, and I admired Dante's ingenuity much as I admired the ingenuity of the inventor of the Palace of Fun at Blackpool, which I visited at about the same time. Oxford marked for me, as for most people, an intellectual decline. I boasted about books there instead of reading them, and, though I can remember often talking about Dante during my undergraduate days, I cannot remember that I ever opened him. But I took him up again when, after going down from Oxford, I was for a time a motor-salesman in Wolverhampton. He is a very good author for motor-salesmen, and if only more of them read him the world would be a better and a happier place. As the Greeks and the mediæval schoolmen truly insisted, a life devoted to selling things rather than to making them is inevitably degraded, and no man can bear it unscathed unless he recreates his mind with the purest thought. Like the drunkard in Manchester, I took to Dante as the shortest way out of Wolverhampton.

I would say that at that time I thought that Dante had an argument, but I thought that it was a silly argument. I did not believe in what I would have called mediæval theories of Heaven and Hell. The notion of the Beatific Vision conveyed no meaning to me, and, while I had very little illusion about the people around me and was quite prepared to agree that they would deserve considerable punishment if ever there should be a judgment, yet I could hardly conceive of anyone being wicked enough to deserve eternal condemnation. I had never met such a person myself and much doubted if he existed. I felt certain that Dante's gay habit of condemning to Hell all his political opponents was nonsensical. I would never have sent anyone to Hell, so why should God? Why should God be so much worse than I was? I therefore would have said at that time that the argument in Dante was his defect. I loved him rather for his historical allusions—such a charming way of picking up the odd strings of history,

> All the charm of all the Muses
> Often flowering in a lonely phrase,

as Tennyson said of Virgil.

It is the superficiality of hedonism that it assumes that it can clearly be predicated of all experiences whether they are pleasurable or painful. It is only of quite superficial experiences that this is so. If we like barley-sugar, then it is pleasurable to suck barley-sugar and there is an end of it. If somebody raps my knuckles with a ruler, that is painful and there is an end of it, but in all deeper things the judgment is not simple. As Euripides taught me at David's death, I found myself 'blest in my unhappiness.' I should have felt miserable if I had not felt miserable. Æschylus had the truth. 'We learn through suffering,' and, with most of us at any rate, almost through suffering alone—and we want to learn and we do not want to suffer. Suffering gives a dignity to man that nothing else can give. It is only in suffering, and in death supremely, that love can be proved. How could we bear one another's burdens if the world were a lotus-eater's world and there were no burdens to be borne? The demand of love is a demand to suffer with the beloved. In a perfect world perfect man would doubtless find other ways of expressing his love, but in an imperfect world imperfect man can only express it in suffering, and, having so expressed it, he values that suffering more highly than all the pleasures which he has enjoyed.

But if a man, and perhaps even more a woman, has this capacity of compassion, whence does it come? The effect cannot be greater than the cause, and if love is in the person then love must be in the nature of things. It has been since the beginning of time the common jest to speak of love as blind, because the lover overlooks all the blemishes in the beloved which are so evident to cooler observers. But it is Dante's startling suggestion that perhaps the exact opposite is true—perhaps it is love alone that is not blind. What God created He created good—it has its 'derived aspect'—its *secondo aspetto*—from God, and good it is in its essential nature in spite of its overlying blemishes. Has not love perhaps penetrated to that essential nature and seen the beloved as she really is, where grosser eyes have been distracted by superficial accidents? This is what Dante believed of his vision of Beatrice. He saw her as she really was, 'smiling, so glad that the joy of God shone out from her face,'

> *Ridendo, tanto lieta*
> *Che Dio parea nel suo volto gloire.*

and through seeing her as she really was he could be led by her at last in the paradisaic vision to see all creation as it really was. 'Not in my eyes only is Paradise,' she could say to him at last, and he, looking around, could see that it was so. '*Ben sem Beatrice*'—'We are Beatrice.'

Reading Dante again with the loss and the longing for Marjorie still fresh upon me, I at last understood the meaning of the great verse. I was working hard at the War Office at the time and had purposely taken on as much work as possible in order to distract my mind by business, but I found myself, dog-tired every night, rushing hurriedly back to the flat to see what new consolations and wonders the *Divine Comedy* might hold for me to-night. It was not only a new planet but a whole new solar system that was swimming into my ken.

The only explanation, according to Dante, of his love for Beatrice, or of my love for Marjorie, or of any boy's love for any girl and any girl's love for any boy, was that love was the law of the universe—not 'creation's final law,' as Tennyson said, but its 'primal' law, or, indeed, as St. John put it, that 'God is Love.' And, if this was so, then a whole new line of answer to the objections which I had raised to George was opened. George had played Blougram to my Gigadibs, and it had been perhaps his fault, if I may say so, that he had been a little too content only to answer the difficulties which I had raised. Dante carried the whole inquiry to a new plane.

There is a relevance about the great poets that, for all its topicality, is wanting in modern literature. Dante is so much more up to date than the headline in to-day's *Daily*

Express, has so much more of practical importance to say than the latest novelist. I will not exactly say that he solved all the questions—whether the particular questions that I raised or others—for obviously the mystery of things cannot be whisked away with some final, glib textbook answer. I distrust such textbook answers. He who thinks that he understands all understands nothing, and, when all the tumult and the shouting of debate, the quiet waiting for the still, small voice, the desolation of the dark night of the soul are done, he has been a very unprofitable inquirer who dares say more than 'Lord, I believe; help Thou mine unbelief.' Yet, if 'God is Love'? I had always up till then thought of this text as a vaguely sentimental way of saying that it was a good plan that we should all be kind to one another. I had been more than a little impressed with the argument of a Chinese professor whom I once met at a tea-party and who had found in the command to love his neighbour his major objection to Christianity. It was, he argued, a barbaric sentimentality. 'We love our relations and a very few dear ones. We have a decent respect, if we are virtuous, for the rights of our neighbours. It is a foolish lie to pretend that we love them.' But suppose that it is in love alone that we see people as they are and without love we do not see them as they are? Dante showed me how God, Who, had He been merely Power, could have had no motive to create, yet had a motive to create through Love. For love alone creates. 'Our Sire in loving begets'—'*Partorisce, amando, il nostre Sire.*'

I saw then, thanks to Dante, what I had never seen before, the true connection between the Old Testament and the New Testament. I had thought of them before as two unconnected stages in the argument. First, you demonstrated that God existed, and then, having got that out of the way, you went on to consider whether Christ was God.

I saw now that the New Testament was the explanation of the Old—that it was only because God was Love that He was able to create the world.

And then Beatrice was dead, as Marjorie was dead, and Bobby Fossett and so many more—

> The many men so beautiful.

Up till now these deaths had seemed to me purely a waste and cause for an explosion of bitterness, and even when I had argued with George about Christ's Resurrection I had not, I think, seen any particular significance in His Death. I had assumed that Christ's argument was, 'I am God, and to prove that I will do a very difficult thing.' And so He had died, and, as was alleged, had risen again from the dead, which was indeed a very difficult thing to do. But, according to my mind—though I had no wish at all to be blasphemous—it would have suited the argument just as well if He had chosen to fly up to the moon on a broomstick and to come down again. I saw no especial significance in death.

But of course there is such a significance,

> Mors et vita duello
> Conflixere mirando.

The creation is a creation of life. Life conquers death, but it can only prove its conquest by submitting to death. Before the Resurrection great men had guessed and proclaimed that the victory was with life, but the Resurrection was needed—the 'wonderful duel'—to give assurance. And if creation was Life and love was creation's law, then love, too, triumphed over death. Beatrice was dead and Dante still loved. Marjorie was dead and I still loved—with a love that could not be overcome but could perhaps be merged into a love of the whole creation if at the last I could see all things as they were.

I do not pretend that I can express all this properly. I speak of a fact and not of a sentimental memory. All this was a few years ago now, and up till the moment of writing I have not yet married again. I have no immediate intention of marrying again. But, on the other hand, I have no principled objection. On principle—though one does not marry on principle—I rather agree with Dr. Johnson that to marry a second wife is a great compliment to the first one, as proving that the condition of matrimony was found agreeable. Yet, whatever new relations may be formed, whatever new facts may come to be, the old fact remains. Death and life have fought in the wonderful duel.

In order to clear my mind I tried to elucidate all this one evening to Tony at the club—not the part about Marjorie (God forbid that I should ever have spoken to him about that), but the part about Dante. The Lord alone knows why I ever tried to do anything so foolish. It was, I need hardly say, a complete failure.

'Oh, so it's all smut, is it?' said Tony. 'I always guessed as much ever since we used to read it up to Bumble, and every now and again I would see him turning over four or five pages and skipping on.'

With so much to despair at, it was hardly worth while to despair at such inanity. I allowed myself to be merely amused and laughed as I protested.

Tony was however, for him, almost serious—more nearly serious than I had ever seen him before!

'But honestly, Peter,' he protested, 'Dante was not married to Beatrice, was he? Well, damn it all, I'm not a moral man—been twice in the divorce courts and all that, you know—but—well—there are limits. All that stuff that you were quoting,

In your eyes
Is Paradise,

all very well on the musical halls, but surely not quite the thing a gentleman would put on paper about a woman who was not his wife!'

George Borthwick was more helpful. Being egotistically concerned with a record of my own progress, I have, I am conscious, up till the present been very far from doing justice to George. He had in our conversations almost confined himself to answering my difficulties and doubtless, though he was never so unkind as to say so, had to a large extent answered a fool according to his folly. But here it was a new George whom I found, a companion on an adventure, an adventure of discovery. George had never known my wife. He had, on the other hand, been Bobby Fossett's most intimate friend. It was therefore natural enough that it was to Bobby rather than to Marjorie that our conversation turned one evening when I was round at his flat. I was still tormented with my fear that it would be found that Bobby and my other friends had, as the somewhat absurdly hackneyed phrase has it, 'died in vain,' that the sacrifice would all prove to have been to no purpose. I appealed to George for comfort.

'Obviously he died in vain,' said George, 'in the sense in which the politicians use one phrase in their speeches. That is to say, no one seriously thinks that this war will end war or that a period of undying peace and prosperity, a world made safe for central heating, is likely to follow immediately after the armistice. Bobby is the last person who ever imagined that it would. The politicians—even the highest of them—think it necessary to hold out all sorts of promises like that to keep people's morale up, and I suppose that these Cabinet-Clowns know their own business. But I should have thought that this was Dawnism of the most cruel type, the deliberate invitation to people to follow a false light, whose failure would be certain to plunge them into despair.'

'To make the world safe for democracy?' he added after a minute, knocking the ashes of his pipe out into the fire. 'Well, it's a matter of simple arithmetic that we shan't do that. In this century all the nations that believe in democracy are going to have falling populations, and all the nations that don't believe in it are going to have rising populations! It's a matter of simple arithmetic, Peter,' he repeated.

'Yes,' I said, 'I can't think how people can fail to see that.'

'Only because after seventy years of compulsory education there are very few people left who can do simple arithmetic,' answered George.

'It's easy enough to see what is the false light,' I said; 'but what is the true light? I agree that the world is not likely to be a very pretty place when this war is over. But, if so, what is the good of it all? Haven't they all died in vain?'

'Oh, well, that's politics,' said George, 'and I don't pretend to know anything about politics. I don't suppose for a moment that the war has done any good. I have never heard of any war that did. It has obviously done a lot of harm, and the world, when it is finished, will be a great deal worse than it was when it began. The case for the war is that it would have been worse still if there had not been a war, and, taking it all in all, I am inclined to think that it would. But that's not what I'm interested in. You know, Peter, my private opinion about politics, and what Carlyle called the-condition-of-the-people question, is that they do not matter very much. I would not write that or say it in the pulpit, because people would so easily misunderstand, and say that I was comfortably off (which I'm not) and therefore did not bother about other people and that I was heartless and a hypocrite and so on. Nevertheless I have little doubt that it is true. Of course there must be government and economic arrangements must be somehow. In a house there must be a lavatory, but that did not make sane the man in *Chrome Yellow* who built all his house round the lavatory. So there must be politics, but that does not mean that they ought to be a preoccupation.'

'Politics are more important than lavatories,' I said.

'Yes, more important,' he agreed, 'but of the same order, or at least the material side of them is. When they challenge the spiritual it is another story.'

'What is important, then?' I asked. 'What is this new gospel that you want to preach?'

'It is not a gospel that I want to preach at all,' said George. 'It's a secret that I want to keep between you and me. I do not think that these things are important. I think that human nature is enormously adjustable and that there is very little reason to think that high standard or low standard of living, good government or bad government, has much effect either on human happiness or human virtue. Take the evidence of art; it does not seem to show any particular relation between high standard of living and *joie de vivre*. Or take the evidence of history—Arnold Toynbee and all that. Civilisations never seem to have crashed out of poverty when the standard of living was low. They always crashed out of boredom when the standard of living was high.'

'Oh, hell, George,' I said, 'if nothing matters, then it seems to me that Pontius Pilate was quite right to wash his hands. It was the most sensible action in the whole story. It was at least hygienic.'

'I never said that nothing mattered,' said George, 'and I said that this was a secret between you and me. I think that it is a good thing that people think that social work matters—not because it does much good to the poor, but because it does a lot of good to the social workers, provided that they are sincere. There are better ways of spending one's life than trying to leave the world a happier place than you found it, but there are also worse ways. And most people would do something worse if they found out our secret—would sink down into mere boredom and slackness and accidie, which is the worst state of all.'

'But the New Testament tells us that the poor are blessed,' I said.

'Yes,' he said, 'blessed and always with you. The New Testament, in impartial rebuke of those who would accept the riches of the rich and those who would abolish the poverty of the poor, suggests that it is a considerable advantage to be poor.'

'But Dr. Johnson . . .' I began.

'Oh, I know Englishmen always think that an argument is ended if they can quote Dr. Johnson. But Dr. Johnson, with all due respect, was not God.'

'I'm sorry, George,' I said, 'but I'm afraid that I just don't get you. I see all the things that you don't believe in, but what is it that you do believe in?"

'I think man's importance is much more restricted than it is the fashion to pretend,' said George. 'How many people are there of whom it can seriously be said that it would make any great difference to human history if they were to drop down dead? Only a very, very few. All except the tiniest handful could obviously be replaced by somebody of the same ability without any great difficulty. On the other hand, there is hardly a person alive whose loss would not be felt in some family or intimate circle. It seems to me that man's duty to these very few neighbours of his family and his immediate friends is as a general rule more important than his duty to society at large. There he really can make happiness or unhappiness.'

'Perhaps,' I said, 'but what has that to do with Bobby Fossett dying in vain?'

'Oh yes, Bobby,' said George, for he had really a bit wandered from the point. 'Well, suppose that life is not really a collective striving after some sort of perfect society at all, but a testing of each individual soul, a warfare between good and evil in the soul. Then the particular circumstances in which the test takes place are secondary—like batting on a sticky wicket or batting on a hard wicket—but the game, the warfare is the thing. The result is again as it may be, but the real triumph is not in victory—I mean external victory—but in showing virtue, and more particularly in showing it where it is difficult to show it—in being brave where one ought to be brave, in being truthful where one ought to be truthful, and cheerful where one ought to be cheerful, and so on. That's why I think that one of the worst things in modern life is *la trahison des clercs,* the quite extraordinary lack of integrity of people who are concerned with opinion—writers, teachers, publishers, journalists. They are always asking only what is immediately sellable and popular, whereas their whole *raison d'être* is to hold up another standard than that of immediate success. The modern intellectual seems to be able to hold simultaneously any number of contradictory opinions, provided only that each one of them is adequately remunerated. There is hardly any justification for publishing anything unless it is going to be rather unpopular. There is no point in telling people exactly what they believe already.'

'Yes,' I agreed. 'I never knew what a racket modern education had become until I met Brakesmith, Martin's headmaster. I never knew that a lot of schoolmasters didn't care twopence whether what they taught was true or not. Whenever Brakesmith put on a new period or got a new textbook, the boys had a joke that he got a rake-off, and on my soul I would not put it past him.'

'Books,' said George, 'should only be written by people who do not need the money from them. There ought to be a sort of amateur status about it.'

'If that's the sort of world that Bobby wanted,' I said, then he did die in vain. For obviously it's not the sort of world that he's going to get.'

'Peter,' said George, 'you're incorrigible. You appeal to immediate results even when you are arguing against immediate results. You are like the American millionaire who said of the Papacy, 'It's not a bad job, but does it lead to anything?' Don't you see that Bobby was the type that believed that virtue was worth while even when he could not see why—in some ways even rather preferred not to be able to see why—like Hector, fighting for Troy, as he used to say?

> 'Tis God shall repay
> I am safer so.

That's the only way that Bobby would have thought that he hadn't died in vain.'

'But, George,' I protested, 'this begs the whole question. Of course he was a fine fellow. We're not disputing that. What I'm asking is, What is the point of his being a fine fellow? What is the good of being good? What do you answer to that? Are you thinking about the Day of Judgment and how good people go to Heaven and bad people go to Hell? You have converted me to a good deal, you know, but I'm not sure if I quite accept all that yet.'

'And you a Dante scholar?' said George. 'Well, there are worse things to think about than the Day of Judgment, but I was not thinking about it for the moment. Quite apart from the Day of Judgment, I think that the showing of virtue does good. You can't quite tell how far the good will spread. It may spread to the most unlikely places, but obviously primarily it does good in the doer's own neighbourhood. Because he showed virtue, it will be easier for his children to show virtue and easier for us to show virtue, and, with that strange paradox that makes up human nature, precisely because Ruth valued him so much she is in a way glad that he has gone. If she had cared less deeply, if he had been to her merely an amusing fellow and a companion, perhaps she would have tried to keep him, but because she was so much a part of him that his honour was her honour she did not try to keep him.'

> 'I could not love thee, dear, so much
> Loved I not honour more,'

I quoted. 'But how did all this question of honour come into it if the war was all rather rubbish?'

'Oh, well, you're a sort of radical,' said George, 'and think that people should make up their own free minds whether wars are right or wars are wrong. I'm afraid my view is that there is a good deal of nonsense and cant about all that. No one but the leaders can possibly know the facts, and even the leaders cannot know what will be the results. Man was made for obedience, and the strength of a country is the possession of people who are willing to come unquestioningly when they are called for. That is what Bobby believed, anyway. So he would have been untrue to himself if he had not acted on it.'

'I don't know, George,' I said. 'All this seems to me rather words going round and round. Do you think that Ruth really saw any sense in his going?'

'You know your own sister better than I do,' said George. 'I should have said that Ruth is not at all politically minded and, like most women, thinks talk about duty to the State highfaluting rubbish, and that she would have seen very little sense in his going if he had not felt that he ought to go, but she saw every sense in his going if he felt that he ought to go. For a Bobby that had not gone then would have been a Bobby minus honour, which would not have been Bobby at all. The more sceptical he was about the war, the more important he thought it not to shirk it.'

'Yes, I think that that's about true,' I agreed. 'I believed in it, and didn't fight it—unless you call going to the War Office fighting.'

I walked across the room and gazed somewhat fatuously at the back of the works of Dr. Hastings Rashdall in the bookshelf. George stuck out his great bedroom slippers towards the fire and leant his elbows upon the arms of his chair like a very weary and angular Titan.

'Of course,' he said, 'speaking seriously, there is a great deal to be said for being killed.'

'What on earth do you mean, George?' I asked, whipping round suddenly.

'Well,' he said, 'there is a sort of sundering dignity of death. Have you noticed how even the most secularist and materialist of men in these days still shudder at desecrating corpses—though on good secularist principles one might well argue that desecration did no harm to anyone and that the prejudice against it was a silly superstition? I suppose that it is because death is the sort of ultimate, the unbeatable, the ace of trumps. If a man complains to us that he is suffering from pain or poverty or bereavement—well, we feel that we, too, have suffered pain and poverty and bereavement, either as bad as he is suffering or worse, or, if we have not had precisely his trial, we tell ourselves that there are plenty of other trials which we have had and he has not. But death is different in kind. A dead man always has an advantage over us. We cannot pretend to have been through that door and no other door is like that door, and at the same time it is important because we will have to go through it one day.'

'Like the Calvinist preacher at Geneva, who said, "*Ah, mes enfants, nous mourrons tous, nous mourrons tous—moi aussi, peut-être,*"' I put in.

'Of course, we think of all the perfectly ordinary and not very brave people who have managed to die fairly decently,'

George went on, 'and therefore we think that we shall be able to carry it off tolerably when our own time comes. But one can never be absolutely sure. And that is why the living always feel a little bit of inferiority when they think of the dead—rather like at school one used to think of people who had actually been to tea with m'dame and come away again, when oneself one was only next on the list to go.'

VII

I OWED, and I owe, a very great deal to George Borthwick. It was he who first taught me what a priest is for—a thing which so many people do not know. It would be ungenerous in me to criticise one who was so very greatly both my intellectual and my spiritual superior. Still, there is no denying it that he was a little 'tomb-minded'—'Long John Donne,' as someone once unkindly described his combination of wooden leg, breezy Silver-like manner and the intellectual equipment of a seventeenth-century metaphysical poet. Of course, if God is good and all His acts are good, then all His acts are good, and there is no more to be said except 'The Lord gave, and the Lord hath taken away; blessed be the name of the Lord.' I am quite prepared to believe that that is the best and the finest faith to hold, but it is only the finest faith to hold if a man does really hold it—as I believe that George did. It is nauseating if an ordinary and unregenerate man merely repeats its formulæ as a hypocritical incantation.

George was always discussing what he called 'the mystery of war.' 'When we want to denounce war-mongers,' he said, 'we call them savage beasts and talk of the law of the jungle. But beasts are just what they are not. The beast in the jungle kills in self-defence or kills for food. Man alone kills when it is not necessary for survival—often kills when he has no notion why he is killing and when it is most doubtful if there is any point in killing. Man is the only animal who does that.'

'Man,' I said, 'and, I am told, the barracuda.'

George, I remember, once said, speaking of superstition, 'There is no superstition more degraded than that of believing that there is an enormous importance in the preservation of one's own life.' I think that there is a good deal in this. I think that there is a lot of absurd exaggeration in this talk about the tragedy of death, and have never myself felt any temptation to take inordinate trouble to avoid it, if it should come my way. When I was at school we read the *Apology* in Upper Division, and I have never forgotten the very sensible remark there of Socrates that some people take so much trouble to escape death on a particular occasion that one might imagine that, if they escaped then, they were going to be immortal. I have great curiosity to know what death really is, and shall be grateful when the time comes to have that curiosity satisfied. Yet, as I have said, 'ripeness is all.' When a man or woman has seen his children grow up to maturity and has done his work in life, then death should be a very reasonable and welcome visitor. The world is indeed often more valuably served by the example of an old age accepted with gracious dignity than by much of the business which is conventionally called work. Nevertheless, a few more years or a few less years of old age are not a great matter. But it is a different issue with those that die before their time—those that die before they have children or before their children have grown up, or those who die when they are themselves children. It is the untimeliness, not the death, that is a tragedy. Those who care to do so can cover the tragedy with the sentimentality that 'they whom the gods love die young,' but this is but a sentimentality and not at all a theological proposition. If man's duty in life is above all to hand on the torch from his father to his children, then indeed it is a tragedy, perhaps the only real tragedy, if he should die before he can do this properly or do it at all.

Perhaps it was my error that I interpreted 'ripeness' in too purely physical a sense. Yet I respected George that he would not try to put me off with a simply glib answer. He would not be drawn. He would neither admit a violation of purpose nor foolishly claim that he fully saw the whole purpose. 'Christianity,' he once said to me, 'is like one of those puzzles when you have to get a lot of quicksilver into a number of holes. There is always a little quicksilver left over.' Thus there was indeed a value in his pegging out of the field, in his exposition of the meaning of things. He made much clear to me that I had not at all understood before. But there is a danger in such a method. The danger is that you will contract reality in your account in order to make it fit in with your lesser pattern of it. Horatio leaves out the things in heaven and earth that he had not dreamed of in his philosophy. But George was never guilty of this fault. He remained always a discoverer, a man to whom had been given the key into the garden of mystery. The planning and the patterning did not with him contract his mind, but rather revealed to him how much there was farther beyond the boundary of the plan. He was like the mountaineer who climbed the height, but only that he might get the vision of the farther height beyond.

He had a great knowledge of stained glass, architecture, sculpture, all the decorations of a church. He always a little reminded me of that line of Lionel Johnson's about Charles I, 'Art to him was joy'—though he was not in the least like Charles I in other ways. I have seen him again nd again peering up through his binoculars at some tained glass at the other end of a church and he would give ne its date at first glance within a matter of twenty years, nd I remember him now when the day we had somehow obained permission to clamber up into the triforium in Wells Cathedral, whence one sees the Jesse window over the altar rom a different height and a different angle from that of he ground. 'Nothing looks more new,' he said, 'than a amiliar thing seen differently. That's why I thought the *Water Babies* such a good book when I was a small boy. Kingsley made the whole village of Harthover look quite lifferent when they looked down on it from on top of a nill. That was right.'

Christianity's judgments are like George's quicksilver. More often than not they coincide with the judgment of numanistic ethics—but not always. Since one of the commands of God is that we do our duty towards our neighbour, there is a rough and general correspondence. As a ule we will not go far wrong, even as Christians, if we sk, 'What is for the general good? Whom am I harming f I do this?' But that correspondence is not invariable. Every now and again God demands sacrifices of the Christian which could not be demanded of him on a secularist code precisely because 'My kingdom is not of this world.'

I remember very well a conversation that I had with Tony. It was a few years ago and quite before I had at all begun to lose my irreligious faith.

'But, good God, Peter,' said Tony, in his hearty way, plashing out the soda, 'surely you believe in birth-control?'

'Of course I don't believe in birth-control as you believe n birth-control,' I said. 'I don't see how anyone outside a unatic asylum could. You mean that the normal thing, when people sleep together, is that they should take precautions to prevent anything coming of it, and that couples

should only try to have children every now and again a
a special treat. With a quarter of the world and a dwind
ling population under the Union Jack and the breedin
barbarians pressing on for Lebensraum, that seems to b
lunacy.'

'But,' I went on, 'I'm not prepared to say that there ar
not circumstances—when for one reason or another it i
impossible to have children—where contraceptives shoul
be used.'

And that position was on its own premises logical, but, i
one accepts Christianity, then one moves on of course int
the fire of a whole new battery of arguments. Choose a
hard, special case and approach the problem merely as a
problem in utilitarianism, and it is indeed often difficul
for an honest man to say where right and wrong lie. Bu
again are these premises sufficient? Is Man such? As I onc
heard Martin remark, 'No one ever suggested that it wa
good for St. Peter's health to be crucified head downwards.

VIII

I WAS not able to get down to see Ruth again until I had
my leave in the October of 1942. Elizabeth, my eldest
daughter, had gone to school in Louisville, so I had though
it best to leave her in America for the duration, but I had
by then brought back the two younger, Monica and Christopher, and they had gone to live with Ruth. I arrived at
the station and was met by Ruth in the governess car
which had now supplanted for station work the petrol
rationed car. Even farmers then by no means had the freedom of petrol which town-dwellers believed.

'How pleasantly Trollopean this all is,' I said, as I
got in.

We trotted off through the town, and then, as we climbed ıt a walk up the little hill beyond it, we made the first :xchanges of family gossip.

'Oh, Peter, my dear,' said Ruth after a few minutes, 'I ıear that George has been converting you.'

'Oh yes,' I agreed, 'there's something in what he says.'

'But, Peter,' she said, 'it's ridiculous. He says that you ıave intellectual integrity and that he learns a lot from alking to you. I can't make it out. I had always known hat you were a dear, sweet thing, but I had never for a noment imagined that you had any sense. Bobby always ısed to say that you had none at all.'

From most people doubtless one would have resented uch a judgment, but I did not in the least mind it from Ruth—not even though I knew that behind all the persi- lage it was perfectly sincere. We had always spoken with nillusioned frankness to one another.

'It's the devil,' I said. 'I was just thinking of setting up s an intellectual on the strength of having read the three ıtest books that are all that anybody in Bloomsbury has ver heard of and along comes George and tells me of undreds and hundreds of more books, and I'm completely ınk.'

'Never mind, dear, we none of us have any brains in our ımily, but we have a knack of hooking on to people who ave them. Are you still Labour, or is that changed ɔo?'

'Oh no, I suppose I'm Labour,' I said, 'for what it may ıean these days.'

'Robert asked Margaret the other day, "What's the abour Party?"' said Ruth. 'Margaret answered, "Oh, it's ɔmething Uncle Peter belongs to." "Oh, is that all?" ıid Robert.'

'It is almost all,' I said.

'I tried to get George down here,' she said, 'but he won't

come because he's got this district down in the East End where he goes and works whenever he gets away from the Ministry of Information. They would never have got their compensation if it had not been for him. He has absolutely saved the lives of those poor people down there.'

'I thought that he didn't see any sense in social work,' I said.

'No, he thinks it probably does not do any good, but there is just an off-chance that it may, so, to be on the safe side, he won't leave it undone. Rich people always think it awfully easy to do good. When they feel pious they call for a cheque-book and a list of charities, and think that some are perhaps a bit better than others, but all are all right, so it does not really matter much. But it does matter a lot both what you give to and how you give. More harm is done by giving wrongly than by anything.'

There was an alert on, and just as we were at the top of Carter's Hill a couple of enemy aircraft flew over.

'I think that we'll just wait for a minute,' said Ruth.

'All right,' I agreed.

But the enemy flew on harmlessly towards the coast and we drove on homewards. We arrived just in time for luncheon, and were greeted by Bertha.

'Hello, Bertha, how's your sister?' I asked.

'Very well, thank you; she's dead,' answered Bertha.

'Oh, but I meant the other one,' I said.

'Oh, the other one,' said Bertha, as if her health was hardly worth an inquiry, seeing that she was alive.

To my surprise and embarrassment I found that my regeneration was the great news of the farm. Ruth said grace before luncheon, and it seems (though I did not know it) that I shut my eyes during its saying. This was indeed a symbol of repentance, and, after lunch was finished, I heard the good news being shouted at least from Aix to Ghent as Robert yelled up the nursery staircase to n children, Monica and Christopher, 'Your daddy isn't an atheist any longer. He shut his eyes during grace.'

'Of course he said his grace,' said Bertha. 'None of your impudence there. I never heard of such a thing.'

Theological preoccupations had soon to give way to the more immediate task of quince picking. There was a quince tree in the garden of this new house, just across the little lawn outside the dining-room window, and with October picking-time had come. My visit provided the opportunity. It is a pleasant task, picking quinces, inviting chatter, confusion and discovery. The sweet smell, oppressive as it may be in a stored, indoors-room, is delightful in the open air, and yellow leaf and yellow tree are of so exactly the same hue that however confidently one feels that the last is picked there is always another found sheltering behind cover. But all depends on the quality of assistance on the ground. The grown-ups—not so much in virtue of their maturity as in virtue of their length of arm—have to climb the ladders and the steps, and perhaps even to venture from them on to the branches themselves. Youth on the ground is there to encourage, to jeer, to receive the plucked quinces as they are handed down, and from time to time to move the steps. My own little children were hardly yet of an age to pretend an interest in the proceedings. Their hearts were wholly lost to the gay Italian prisoners who worked in the neighbouring quarry, and, in intelligent anticipation of a co-belligerency to come, they had even sewn neat little patches on to their trousers in order the more realistically to play the game of being prisoners of war. After a glance of scorn to convince themselves that their new-found father was still a buffoon, as I vanished into the leaves, they betook themselves off hand in hand to their own game, which was that of pretending to be grown-ups and each boasting to the other of the size of their family.

'I'm fifty-one, three times as old as Daddy, and have eight children, all four years old,' proudly announced Monica. 'How many children have you got, Christopher?'

'Only two,' said Christopher. 'Five died.'

Ruth's children, being somewhat older, did keep themselves technically in action by lurking round the foot of the steps and receiving a quince, when their attention could be attracted. Yet at the same time they conducted a conversation hardly less inconsequent.

'Uncle Dotty, when he was a boy, once climbed up in a damson tree and he fell out and broke hisself,' announced Robert as a twig snapped under my hand.

'Robert,' said Ruth, from the other ladder, 'I've told you before that I will not have you calling your great-uncle "Dotty."'

'Oh, but it's just what he is, you know, Mummy dear,' said Margaret. 'He's not decent like Uncle Peter.'

'Thanks awfully, Margaret,' I said from among the leaves. 'I always knew that you were a friend. What size tip do you expect for that?'

'It would be rather fun seeing Uncle Dotty fall out of a damson tree,' said Margaret. 'I really shouldn't awfully mind if he hurt himself.'

'I should like him to stay in the damson tree for ever,' announced Robert, 'and never be able even to fall out.'

A quince, shaken off its branch before it was plucked, bounced down the leaves and eventually landed on Robert's head at the foot of the steps. Back-chat was temporarily dissolved in objurgation.

'I must say that your children are very foul-mouthed,' I said to Ruth approvingly. I have always distrusted good language.

'Yes, they have been brought up to be,' she said.

'Robert's language is getting disgraceful,' said Bertha, who, as was her custom when any brouhaha was on, had abandoned the washing-up and presented herself arms akimbo and for comment. Faithful as she was, she always had a certain feeling that things in Barston had been slightly queer ever since Bobby's father died. While no one could call her a formal dresser herself, yet the upper classes, she felt, ought to dress up. That's what they were for—Conservatism ought to be sartorial as well as ideological—and gentlemen ought to swear to one another but not before ladies or the servants.

'Your grandfather,' she told Robert, 'used to swear something terrible, but not before us. We had to listen outside when we wanted to hear what he said.'

After dinner that evening, when the children had retired and peace at last reigned, I asked Ruth how fortune was treating her.

'Oh, it's a grand life this, Peter,' she said. 'I wouldn't miss it for anything. The people are fine, and one really can make both ends meet now in war, which was more than Bobby could ever do in peace-time.'

I must say that the life did seem to suit her—a great deal more than life in the War Office suited me. Indeed, the contrast between both the pleasantness and the usefulness of our two lives was so poignant that I sometimes felt that I hardly could bear to visit her—that if one is compelled to be in a cage for nine-tenths of life it is better to be there for ten-tenths and to forget that there still is a world of sanity. When I saw her standing by the gate, her Wellingtons up to her knees cased in mud and dung, dirty open shirt, bellowing, as it might be, at hens or cows or children, I could not but feel mad with envy. The refined may say that the picture is not altogether a refined one, and indeed there is no denying that the life had in one sense coarsened her. At the best of times she was not what I call a 'washy' girl. She wallowed in a daily bath, but was not one of those who are for ever washing their hands, even though there be nothing to wash about. Now she washed more than she had in her lady's life, for every time that she came in her occupation compelled washing. Yet there was certainly an atmosphere of dirty boots about the house, and it was no longer required of air to be fresh that it bring no odour with it. The children, both mine and hers, were most obviously of the earth. There reigned over all an air of fecundity in confusion, where the same name might apply indifferently to a pig, a daughter, a duckling or a pony. I do not mind all that. I like to dress up and be clean and to go to a party every now and again, but I like to be as if one were dressing in a play. For every day I prefer old clothes and a moderate coarseness.

The people of the village, too, did seem extraordinarily nice. There was Bertha, like the nurse in *Romeo and Juliet*, who had cooked for the family since the days of Bobby's father. She slopped round the house all day in bedroom slippers and with her greying hair wisping all over her face. Talk of rationing she treated as an insult to which she would not deign even to reply, and it was a hard task indeed to make her confine her cooking at all within the limits of the available, to say nothing of the legal. Wars, she felt, were not what they used to be. 'There was nothing like this in the Boer War.' Uncle Dotty detested her. 'The servants speak to me,' he complained. 'It is intolerable.' But the rest of us reckoned garrulity a small price to pay for such kindness and faithful service. A more serious vice was her habit of playing the wireless in the kitchen all day long and usually untuned and with two stations at once but even that was to be tolerated for the sake of peace. There were the men on the farm, Perkins, the carter, Hands, the shepherd, and the two boys, Tom, Hands' nephew, and Geoffrey, who had come at the beginning of the war as an evacuee with his parents from Stepney, wher[e] he had never in his life seen a green field. He had let hi[s] parents return and stayed to become a farm-hand, determined, for all his odd notions, never to return to London. There were other strange, noble souls among the villagers. It is often said of the English village that it is a hotbed of snobbery where the poor man at the gate sits snarling enviously at the rich man in his castle, like the Russians in Seton Merriman's *Sowers*. It is often also said that there is a dull sameness about the villagers' clod-like lives. There are, I know, villages of which both these charges would be true, but it was not, as far as I could see, at all true of Barston. There was rather an abundant variety in its characters, a free outspokenness in its life. The men, for the most part, uncomplainingly manned the Home Guard, where gentlemen farmers and retired army officers served under the command of the local grocer. The atmosphere of the Home Guard was what politicians call democratic and human beings call friendly. Like the men in every other village in England, they manned the hills at night and peered through the dark for descending German parachutists. Like the men in every other village in England, they saw none.

But the village had also its little family of Christadelphian pacifists, and no one thought the worse of them, for they were known to be sincere 'and not just shirkers.' And there was Pat, the Irish labourer, who had lost one son at the Somme in the last war and another on the *Audacious* in this and who 'thanked God that de Valera had kept us out of the war.' 'As Cardinal Newman used to say,' he would remark, 'it's just one damned thing after another.' Nor did many think much the worse of the baker, who lived in sin with his lady, refusing again to enter a church ever since the Rector—the last Rector but two—had argued with the umpire when he was given out l.b.w. Even those who did not agree with him in his apostasy yet agreed that the reason was a good one. They were a pious people, but to them the purpose of piety was to please the Rector, and the purpose of impiety was to annoy him, and those who argued when they were given out l.b.w. deserved to be annoyed.

The war had brought a new and strange form of charity into English rural life. Men and women of the utmost respectability, who before the war would have died sooner than break a bye-law, in war-time defied regulations in order to pass kindly from hand to hand illicit little stocks of eggs or cheese or milk or meat. It was in this typically English way that the English fought their battle against totalitarianism, and the number of benefits that Ruth thus received from her neighbours was only equalled by the number of benefits that she conferred. 'I expect I shall go to prison for it, Mrs. Fossett, but never mind,' was the continual greeting to her of her kindly neighbours as the little gift was passed or the little service rendered.

I do not want to romanticise these people. The village had its black sheep—an idle beer-swiller, a good-for-nothing poacher, one unfriendly farmer-neighbour, a loafer, of whom it was said that you had always to watch him lest he should scamp his work. Even of those I liked I do not pretend that all of them were faultless saints. And yet I was, and am, amazed at their friendliness and at their readiness to help Ruth in countless little ways. Whether it was because of the influence of Bobby or the appeal of chivalry—of Ruth's widowhood, or just because of natural kindness or the absence of the motor-bus, I cannot say, but there the blessed virtue was.

'One gets,' said Ruth, 'a much greater variety of company through living in a little village.'

This seemed to me a paradox, but she stuck to her point.

'Of course, there are all sorts in London,' she conceded, 'and a few people take the trouble to see all sorts. But most people, taking the line of least resistance, sink into only consorting with their own sort. Barristers only see barristers, and writers only see writers, and politicians politicians, and cut-throats cut-throats, and archdeacons archdeacons. It's a very narrow life. How often do you go down to the East End?'

'Marjorie often used to go,' I said.

'Ah, yes,' said Ruth, 'but then Marjorie was rather an exception. But in the country everybody has to know everybody because there's nobody else to know.'

I asked her about the men who worked for her, and she gave me her report on them.

'We've managed all right so far mainly thanks to Billy Perkins,' she said. 'But things are going to be a bit more difficult in the future. In a few months both Tom and Geoff will be off to the Navy, and I shall be off to prison the way things look now.'

'I can understand about Tom and Geoff going to the Navy,' I said, 'but why should you go to prison?'

'Oh, haven't you heard?' said Ruth. 'I've taken it into my head to do a village-Hampden stunt. They wanted me to fill up a form about Tom and Geoff's call-up and on it I had to give every sort of information to them both about myself and about all the men that work for me. If I was trying to get the two boys exempted, I could see that there might be some point in making me give every detail about my labour, but, since I do not want to get them off and the boys don't want to get off, I don't see why I should go round asking all the men their ages and doing the Government spies' work for them.'

'The spies have plenty of other ways of finding out people's ages,' I said. 'You need not think that you can keep it from them like that.'

'Oh, I know that,' said Ruth, 'but I don't see why I should help them to find out. I haven't got any political principles, but I have real anti-political principles, you know, Peter. I do think it important that a few people should stand out against meekly doing every single thing they tell one to do. I don't suppose I'll really go to prison for a moment. The paper seems to say that you will go to prison if you make a false return, but they have forgotten to say what happens if you don't make a return at all. But I think honestly that I would be prepared to go to prison about a thing like that.'

'Well, think honestly then, my girl,' I said a little unkindly, 'and good luck to you, because it's quite certain that you won't have to go. In the first place, they're pretty fair fools, but they aren't quite fools enough to lock up Bobby's widow on a charge like that. In the second place, the first thing that they want is for people to run their farms. Odd as it may seem, there are some people even in the Board of Agriculture who think that more important than filling in forms—not that they don't doubtless think you a cranky nuisance for refusing to fill up their muck. So I dare say that on balance you are doing some good.'

The next day we met the two boys digging to drain off some of the rain from a low-lying field. They were pleasant spoken, if slightly gauche, boys. When we had gone on I asked Ruth about them.

'Oh, they're both good lads,' said Ruth, 'but very different from one another. It's rather interesting comparing them.'

'How so?' I asked.

'Tom is the children's friend because he climbs trees and gives them rides on his bicycle. I don't know what effect the Navy will have on him, but at any rate at the moment he has never done anything but live on a farm and has no idea of living anywhere except on a farm. When he was at school they tried to give him some sort of scholarship to keep him there, but his own idea was to leave as soon as possible to get back to the farm. He's a great worker.'

'He seems ideal,' I said.

'He almost is as far as I'm concerned,' said Ruth, 'but you mustn't think that he is in every way a paragon of virtue. He is a bit of a lad of the village, and the Rector's got his knife into him. There are terrible rumours that he drinks beer at the pub, and indeed once or twice he has appeared a bit late for work and looking a trifle like the morning after the night before.'

'And Geoff?' I asked.

'Oh, he's painfully respectable as far as morals go—doesn't drink and doesn't smoke and, they say, even doesn't swear. But for all the way that he's taken to the land, he's still a Cockney. He thinks I'm very rum because I'm not always bothering about saleability. We must have large apples and large potatoes and big eggs and large white loaves, milled between steel rollers. The customers like them big, he always says. "Oh, but Geoff," I keep saying to him, "you know as well as I do that small apples are better than large because the nearer the fruit is to the core the better." And, "Oh, Geoff, it's much better for the hens to lay small eggs than large." And, "Oh, but, Geoff, if you use chemical manure for the potatoes, of course you get a bigger vegetable in the raw, but when you boil it it goes black and boils to nothing." And, "Oh, but, Geoff, if you make a loaf of strong wheat, it looks bigger because there's more water in it, but there's really more food in the smaller loaf of the weak wheat." But he only answers, "I don't know anything about that, Mam, but the public likes things big. Of course, we can set a few rows of potatoes for ourselves without the chemical manure, but the public likes 'em big." After the war he's going to be a chemist.'

'Why? Does he know any science?' I asked.

'Oh, I don't mean a scientist. I mean a man in a shop. He says that people buy more drugs than food, and they are in more of a stew when they buy them and more people are ill than well. So it stands to reason that there is more money to be made out of being a chemist than a farmer.'

'I read the other day that the nation's bill for medicine is just half its food bill,' I said. 'I shouldn't be surprised if Geoff proved quite right. It's all the education.'

'Yes, too much of it,' she said. 'The country boys are to some extent inoculated to it, because they can see that it's nonsense before their eyes, but the town boys believe it all.'

'Oh, come, Ruth,' I said, 'it's awful nonsense this running down of education. I didn't mean that.'

'Some things in education may be all right,' said Ruth, 'but what seems so wrong in it, as it is now, is that they teach people to price things rather than to value them. They seem to come out of those schools thinking that nothing is worth anything for its own sake, but only worth what money it will fetch in a market.'

'Well, I would sooner that they taught them to market potatoes than taught them to market themselves, like that old fool at Martin's school did,' I said.

'It's difficult to know what one ought to do in practice,' said Ruth, 'especially when one is a parent. It's all very well to have eccentric ideas and all very well to hope that one's children will have reasonably eccentric ideas, but I don't think that one has a right to impose eccentricity on them. Take Margaret. There is nothing that I disapprove of more than sending girls away to school. Before you know where you are they will be feminists and want to have careers and refuse to have children and grow beards and wear hard collars.'

'It did not seem to have that effect on you,' I said.

'Oh, well, I didn't really go to school,' said Ruth. 'I always used to hide in the lavatory when they did arithmetic and just came out for history—rather like the badger sleeping all winter and waking up for the summer. Mine was not really an education; it was just a training in anarchy.'

'Well, it didn't do you any harm,' I said.

'That's hardly for me to say,' said Ruth. 'Tony said to his constituents one day that he stayed at school till eighteen and it never did him any harm. Well, I don't know if it was staying at school till eighteen or what, but something has certainly done him quite a lot of harm.'

'Having too much money,' I said.

'Perhaps,' said Ruth. 'Well, Margaret won't suffer from that, at any rate. Anyway, there she was at fourteen—a certain smattering of letters from a governess so that you could just say that she was not illiterate in either English, French, Latin or Italian, every now and again coming out in all innocence with the most highly unladylike expressions picked up on the farm, rather dirty, sometimes spitting on the floor, really useful on the farm, knowing everything that there was to be known about animals and crops by a sort of second nature. Was there any sense in changing all that?'

I remembered the truly superb facility with which I had seen her turn an enormous cheese alone, whisking round the cloth by a trick of hand, and I shared every doubt.

'The trouble was,' Ruth went on, 'that she did from time to time get a bit moody and want more female companionship of her own age. It was not that I thought that school would really do her much good, but I thought that, if she never went to school, she might grow up with a grievance against life and perhaps a grievance against me because she had missed something. That's why I sent her to that convent.'

'I never understood why you chose a convent,' I said.

'Because I thought that nuns would be less careery than ordinary schoolmistresses,' said Ruth, 'but I don't know that they are. They seem to have an absurd respect for the world outside their enclosure. Still, she likes the school on the whole, and I don't think it's done her any harm. She's at home just now for a week or two because of this infection, but she will be quite glad to go back again. It's only the farm that will miss her.'

IX

THAT afternoon the prospective Liberal candidate came to tea. The day has passed when Nonconformist shopkeepers could be persuaded to put up as Liberal candidates. Nonconformist shopkeepers have far too keen a sense of the practical and the attainable to be willing thus to waste their time upon forlorn hopes. The Liberal Party to-day, or, as the case may be, the Liberal Parties, are the last home of the eccentric gentleman—an admirable and wholly necessary class. It is a solid and sober fact of history that never has the cause of democracy been successfully pleaded except by men of aristocratic origins, and some of the most colourful pages of Europe's story have been those which record the fights for liberty of aristocratic adventurers. They have done harm, too, of course—these Liberal aristocrats—but there is everything to be said for them, so long as there are not too many of them. It seems a far cry from dying in the swamps of Missolonghi or storming Sicily with the Thousand to being a Parliamentary candidate for a West Country constituency at a time when there is not an election. But there is the same authentic note about all the adventures—the note of forlorn hope.

Michael Paravane was a gallant, laughing, gay, rather intelligent young man of about twenty-nine. He drank like a fish in an absent-minded sort of way—the way in which

I suppose, fish do drink—putting down whatever came before him without much noticing it and without turning a hair. He had fought bravely throughout the first year of the war, but had been badly wounded at Dunkirk and had been invalided out of the army. He was now Private Secretary to the Other Liberal, who was in the Cabinet, because some Liberal had to be.

As these pages have already shown, I am, God knows, muddle-headed enough about politics to have forfeited all right to laugh at others. Yet there was, I always found, something wholly ludicrous, if wholly attractive, about Michael's unwavering confidence that all the political troubles of the world could have been solved by a few comparatively small legislative changes of the right sort. 'If only Ramsay Macdonald had brought in Proportional Representation in 1923 none of this would ever have happened,' he murmured, a fellow-officer told me, as he cowered in a sand-pit on the Dunkirk shore, one moment before an exploding bomb blew him into insensibility. He was an old-fashioned Liberal—a liberal Liberal, as he would put it—who really believed in human freedom and free trade and opposition to state interference. He was also a Catholic. I never knew before that Catholicism and Liberalism could be combined, but he seemed to find it possible. He was a kindly, lovable man, boundless in his human sympathies, and was the only person I ever heard of who had an affection for King George I.

Bobby and he never went to the poll together, as he was only adopted as the prospective candidate a few months before the war, but Bobby always got on well with his political opponents, and at once a firm, if slightly ironical, friendship had sprung up between them. 'He's kindly, greedy, lazy, uncharitable; he has all the attractive qualities,' said Bobby. 'Poor Michael,' he added, 'he has no sense of public life as a menagerie.' 'Nor is it,' I said, for

I had in those days still a lurking respect for politicians and was sometimes a trifle irritated by the virulence with which in Bobby familiarity had bred contempt.

He was a neighbour of the Fossetts, from the next village. He lived in a rambling, ramshackle old Jacobean house, where big rooms had been partitioned off into small rooms with bewildering confusion, and bedroom led out of bedroom in such proliferation that it was, as Tony said, almost impossible not to commit adultery even if one tried. But, as with the war his own house—with the exception of one bedroom and one sitting-room—was entirely taken over by a negro pioneer corps, he was glad enough when he got down from London to find his social amenities at the Fossett farm. He came over on a bicycle and stayed to tea. It was more than the desire for company which had brought him out this afternoon. He had heard of Ruth's refusal to sign the form about the calling-up of the two youths, and was all agog with excitement.

'You won't weaken, will you, Ruth?' he pleaded. 'Promise me that you won't sign it.'

'Are you on the bench, Michael?' I asked him.

'No, I'm not,' he said; 'but, anyway, J.P.s don't have anything to do with a case like that.'

'Oh, I thought that you might say a good word for me,' said Ruth.

'But, Ruth,' he said, 'there's no chance of your getting off, is there? I mean to say—that would spoil everything. This is a real election cry. I honestly believe that I can carry the constituency on this, particularly with you being a Conservative, which makes it seem all so much more disinterested. I really think that we might even start a Midlothian campaign on it and sweep the country. I must speak to Billy and see what he thinks about it.'

Billy was the Other Liberal, the Cabinet Minister, his boss in London.

'Oh, bother,' said my young Christopher, who was sprawling out at length on the rug and taking up all the fire.

'Why do you say bother?' we all asked.

''Cos Mr. Paravane won't go,' announced Christopher. 'I want Aunt Ruth to read to me.'

The slight awkwardness caused by his pronouncement was smoothed out with apologies, and the thread of the argument resumed.

'But surely I must be allowed to have a point of view,' said Ruth.

'Oh, you needn't worry,' said Michael. 'I'm told that it's really awfully nice in Brixton. You can get up when you like, and there are debtors, who are in for contempt of court, who will wait on you if you pay them.'

Michael himself had Fenian blood from his mother's side and always carried about with him a great contempt for people who had never been in prison. I have never myself been able to see the moral superiority of jug *per se.*

'But who will look after the farm?' I asked.

'Yes, there is that,' said Michael.

He pensively bade us farewell, reflecting on the malign fate which always erected some obstacle to every scheme for the great Liberal revival.

I was glad to take the opportunity when I came down to Barston to learn philosophy at the feet of that very wise and noble man Billy Perkins, the cowman. To the children Hands the shepherd was the great friend and counsellor, and indeed there was to be culled from Hands an abundant store of particular wisdom, of wise saws and ancient instances, of anecdote and remedy, but to maturer taste there was a deeper wisdom and a deeper understanding to be found in Billy Perkins. Without knowing that he did so, he cut through and challenged so much of all modern political clamouring by his utter absence of envy. Alike in all the modern demands for equality of opportunity and in the opposition to it, it is assumed that everybody wants a higher standard of living, as it is called, if possibly he can get it. The one side asks why he should not have it, and the other talks of killing the goose that lays the golden egg if a reward for enterprise is not permitted. To Billy Perkins both philosophies were alike absurdities. The theoretical Marxian might say perhaps that it was because he had a slave's soul that he was content, but a man who, having seen Billy Perkins, could still say that he had a slave's soul would, like the Duke of Wellington's friend, say anything. He was content because he was content. He had sufficient to eat. He had work that occupied his interest. What more did a man need? And, if he needed no more, what madness to fret for it? He did not of course say all this in so many words, but it was implicit in all his commentary.

'If people work in a factory,' he said, 'they know when they are working and they know when they are playing. They are working when they are in the factory and not working when they are not in it. That life's all wrong. People ought to do a lot of things that nobody can quite say whether they're a part of work or not—like when you was picking quinces, or when I go round with the children, showing them how to plough or how to make a silo.'

If he had a fault it was that he was perhaps a little too contemptuous of those who surrendered in any way to the utilitarian standards of the day. He was, I thought, for instance, a bit hard on poor Tom, who, in a world where boys were paid £3 a week, was glad enough to get his £3 a week, and, as I have said, apparently spent a reasonable proportion of it in the Abbot's Arms.

'Them boys,' he said, 'what do they want with three pound a week? When I were married I got thirteen shilling a week, and lucky to get it.' (This can't be quite true, but it was what he told me—what, by constant repetition, he had certainly persuaded himself, even as George IV had persuaded himself that he had fought at the Battle of Waterloo—for I several times heard him say it.) 'What does that lad want with going off to the Abbot's Arms? When I were a lad no bigger than your Christopher I used to go to the Abbot's Arms of an evening and they gave me sevenpence to wash up the glasses, but I never been in there since, man and boy.'

I could only reflect how very few of the glasses would have survived if Christopher had the washing of them.

Billy Perkins was, as such men are apt to be, a pessimist about the rising generation.

'Ah, and they won't get married now,' he said. 'There's sure to be goings-on if they don't get married. But they won't get married because of the teeth.'

'Because of the teeth, Mr. Perkins?' I asked, quite out of my depth.

'Ay, yes,' he said, 'because of the teeth. Before a lad will marry a girl he wants her to have her teeth out and to have false ones in, and paid for by her parents. He doesn't want that expense to come on him just when the kids are growing up. But now, what with this war and all, you can't get teeth, and these lads, they won't marry without 'em and they won't wait. I suppose it's all Nature.'

'What's Nature, Mr. Perkins?' I said. 'False teeth?'

He looked at me with a certain contempt. Such men dislike, perhaps rightly, being thrown off the slow development of their argument by verbal quips or repartees or confusions.

'You deal fair with Nature,' he said, 'and Nature will deal fair with you. Take dung.'

Though I did not, I must confess, quite see its relevance to the argument, yet dung was just what at the time we were taking. We were during this conversation engaged on the building of a dung heap and I, a humble disciple, was learning many mysteries of this great art which I had not hitherto suspected. The great authority—or at the least the great theorist—of the village upon dung was Armstrong, the pub.-keeper. Armstrong was, as I have said, a bit of a freethinker and a radical, and also a great one for the preaching to the less lettered of the new dodges and methods which he had read of in books and magazines. At the moment he was full of the Indore process of manuring, and had expounded it to me the previous evening in the Abbot's Arms. I had been stupid about it to begin with, thinking that it was called the 'indoor' process and was therefore rather disgusting. Armstrong reassured me on its Indian name, its traditional nature and its proven value to the land.

The site of a heap, Armstrong insisted, must be selected with all the care with which one might choose a cricket pitch. You must find, he said, an angle between two walls in the kitchen garden which faced conveniently to the south and was sufficiently protected from the cold and wind.

'You must make your heap five feet broad and five feet long and four and a half feet high for a garden heap,' he said. "Thirty feet long and fourteen feet broad and four and a half feet high for a farm heap.'

'You don't start with dung,' he explained to me, as a patient mistress might explain the alphabet to a very dull infant. 'You start with vegetable rubbish and leaves and twigs, and maybe some old hay or straw, a piece or two of bracken, if there's some about; then some old clothes, if you soak them all in water first. Old clothes is, in a manner of speaking, a sort of dung. Then you put some dung and some dirty earth on top of that. You must always mix the vegetable and the animal. Six inches vegetable, two inches dung and then a layer of dirty earth, and then all over again until you have got it to the right height, but you must finish off with a double thickness of dung and then an earth cover.'

'Yes,' I said, 'and what then?'

'Don't stamp on 'er, Mr. Smith'—he always called me Mr. Smith, having no time for the refinements of a double name, just as in a similar spirit of realism he always referred to dung in the feminine—'don't stamp on 'er, Mr. Smith. How can the air get at 'er if you stamp on 'er? Then give her just a sprinkling of water from the nozzle and then we make three vents with the crowbar and then the heap's done.'

I tried Armstrong's theories out on Billy Perkins the day after their exposition. I had expected the scorn of the conservative practitioner for the radical theorist, but I found, a little to my surprise, that Billy, though he despised Armstrong's radicalism about people, had some respect for his agricultural theories. 'Armstrong doesn't like people,' he explained, 'but he likes the land.' And Billy was no obstinate conservative, but most open-minded about all schemes for the improvement of the land, provided only that it was a land-lover who propounded them.

'But surely, Mr. Perkins,' I said, 'it isn't every farmer who takes as much trouble about his dung as you do. I don't know that I've ever seen anybody else take so much trouble about it.'

'There ain't anybody else that takes that much trouble about her,' he said, 'not one farmer in all Somerset—not even,' he added with that strange nostalgic phrase of his which was in his mouth the cream of all superlatives, 'not even in Epsom. But you can't be too careful with dung.'

He had once been to Epsom, and this reminiscence of travel remained ever afterwards the supreme comparison on his tongue.

'And I suppose that you're one of those who think that artificial manures are no good,' I said.

I knew all the theories that Bobby had picked up about the waste of the soil and the law of the return, and, though he had picked them up mostly in America, I knew well that he would not have been allowed to pick them up had not Billy Perkins approved.

'Artificial manure—it comes in good for making explosives,' he said.

He agreed with Armstrong that, if we have to import, it is much better to import the cattle food, which the cattle will turn into the dung that makes humus, rather than the artificial manure which destroys the humus.

'You can't,' he said, 'you can't deal ungracious with dung.'

As we walked down through the forty-acre field, Billy Perkins developed to me his theories about ley-farming.

'You've got a great deal more under the plough than there used to be in Mr. Fossett's time,' I said.

'Ah, yes,' he said, 'this ain't rightly an arable part of the country, but it's a good thing to have something ploughed, for all that. Farms ought to be about half and half—arable and meadow—and all different sorts of animals so as to have different sorts of dung. You must have arable, if not for the humans, then for the animals.'

He was scornful of the lazy folk who thought that grass was merely grass and that, once a field had been allowed to go to grass, there was no cause to worry about the sort of grass that grew there. On the contrary, he thought that the plough should go round practically the whole farm in its proper and ordered sequence and that this system should be based on leys of from two to about six years' rotation. Only really hopeless rough grazing land should be left to permanent pasture.

'But where do you find that,' he said, 'except on the Tweedside? And,' he added almost fiercely, as if it was an insult that such experiments should be carried on behind his back, 'I never was there. I read about it all once in a book, but I never was there.'

Where he thought that the improvement really was an improvement no one clamoured for it more pertinaciously than he.

'It's the land that matters, Mr. Smith,' he said to me. 'Yes, it's the land that matters.'

This, I found, was the basis, the complete rationalisation of all his prejudices. He did not think that man had any business to aim directly at his own happiness. His duty was to serve the land, and happiness would perhaps be the uncovenanted reward of faithful service. Again, of course, I make explicit what was to him entirely instinctive. But it was by this test of the land's well-being that everything was to be judged—social and political programmes, wages and systems of land tenure, new schemes and tools in agriculture. If the land was the better for them, they were to be welcomed. If the land was the worse for them, they were to be condemned.

Thus I tried him with theories of peasant proprietorship, but it was clear that here were book terms and ambitions to which he was wholly unaccustomed. For all his devotion both to the land in general and to locality, he had yet had no wish himself to own. He had never envisaged a world in which he did not work for a farmer, who was in his turn kept in his place by a squire. Devoted as he was both to Bobby and to Ruth, he had yet no illusions either about farmers or about squires in general. Still, he had no doubt that that was the best system.

'No, Mr. Smith,' he said, 'men like me, we can do our job, but we can't see things in the balance, like a more superior person can. How would a shepherd like Hands know whether trees ought to be planted? And how would we know what a house ought to be like? No, Mr. Smith,' he repeated, 'it needs a more superior person. All the manor-houses being empty, or full of niggers like Mr. Paravane's—it ain't right—it ain't right at all. It needs a more superior person.'

But didn't he agree, I asked, that people ought to be equal?

No, he agreed to nothing of the sort. 'No, Mr. Smith,' he said, 'that ain't sensible noway.'

Then I tried him with Socialism. I agreed with him that peasant proprietary could not altogether meet the case and that there must be some central direction of wider vision. But would it not be a good plan that the land should be owned by all and for the good of all and the direction be in the hands of those who wielded it not for private profit, but for the general good?

These were to him words and of little meaning. Who was it who would have power behind this façade of verbiage? That was the question with which, I could see, his mind was occupied. What reason was there to think that they would be concerned only with the general good, whatever that might mean? Would they love the land? If, as he shrewdly suspected, they would be politicians and townsmen and London folk, aping for the votes of yet more townsmen behind them, then how could such people, who were not of the land, ever love the land?

'When the war come,' he said, 'they told us to kill off our pigs because there was no food for them. And they told us to stop hatching fresh broods of chickens, and then they told people to keep hens. And then they let us have the hens, but would not let us have the food for the hens. No, that ain't sensible at all, not nohow!'

Oh, the multitudinous sins of 'they'!

'No, Mr. Smith,' he said, 'it wouldn't do; it wouldn't do at all.'

Michael Paravane in his crazy enthusiasm had started just before the war a sort of agricultural settlement on his estate, and people in long hair and dressed in smocks had come down and sung country songs and danced country dances. It was perhaps neither fair to Bloomsbury nor to Whitehall to think that for better or for worse the Civil Servants, whose minutes never ended, bore any resemblance to these poets, whose verses never scanned. Yet Billy Perkins had got it firmly into his head that this was what 'Lunnon folk' were like and that they were 'plain daft.' By their test all large planning stood to him condemned.

'When I were a lad,' he said, 'there were a woman came down from London to live at Cary, Lady May Something her name was, and she said that she always liked to see corn growing in the fields outside her window. So she said she'd pay Farmer Passmore if only he'd grow corn in they fields every year.'

He relapsed into a sort of restrained chuckle—a compound of laughter at London folly and horror at London wickedness—the wickedness which sets love of a view before love of the land.

The young generation in Barston, as elsewhere, was at that moment scattered over every continent and ocean. It would ill become one who, slightly older than they, had stayed at home to accept Billy Perkins' strictures upon them. And if those on the distant frontiers did not deserve them, no more, I think, did those slightly younger who still remained at home. I dropped in to the Abbot's Arms on Sunday evening at about nine o'clock to greet old Armstrong. The Home Guard was there. They had been having a field-day that morning against the Welsh Guards, and their commanding officer, the local grocer, had succeeded in making military history by getting himself taken prisoner twice in a single morning. Captured in the first minutes of the battle, he had been let go free in order that he might make a fight of it, and had been duly captured again a few minutes before lunch. There were some who felt this as a deep disgrace. To others, the more irreverent, it was a cause of laughter. The argument flew to and fro. The rounds were called for. Then the conversation switched. A banjo appeared—God knows where from—and the fun became louder and louder. The songs were neither traditional folk-songs, nor the songs of the last war, nor the songs of the music halls, but pleasant, bawdy catches were bawled at the ceiling in a manner that was refreshing and not unElizabethan. They had largely come from the American neighbours, quartered in the next village, among whom, whether they be black or white, singing to-day flourishes more than it does among us. A continually reiterated command to 'lay that pistol down, baby' filled the din of the bar. It is the most ominous of all commentaries on our life that this war should be fought with the songs of the last war. I was grateful even to 'a pistol-packing mama' who had in part rescued us from that reproach.

Tom was, of course, of the drinking company that night, even as, equally, of course, Geoff and still more Billy Perkins were not. There is no accounting for heads, and therefore it is never for one man to say with confidence whether another is sober or not. But I should have thought it difficult for even the weakest head to get drunk on wartime beer. Of course, he shouted a bit louder and talked a bit more than he would normally have done. So did I. So did we all. I am of the school of the Greek poet Theognis, who thought that it was very bad manners to be drunk in the presence of the sober or sober in the presence of the drunk. And had the party of his elders and betters been a drunken party, I should not have held it much against a boy of eighteen had he been a trifle excited too. But it was my belief that when Armstrong turned us out into the dark at a rather unpunctual ten, neither Tom nor anybody else was in the least drunk.

'Ah,' Armstrong confided in me, 'Billy Perkins is a bit

hard on the young folk. But then he's old-fashioned. Last time he were in a pub, he told me, was in 1893. "Well," I said to him, "in 1893 beer was beer and drink was drink." But he doesn't take in how different things is now. Why, I haven't had a white man drunk in here since Christmas—not even an American.'

I reflected how false was the legend of the dumb, tongue-tied countryman. The truth is rather that he talks about different things from the Cockney. The Cockney cannot understand his language, nor he the Cockney's. But he does not expect to understand the Cockney and passes him by as of another race. He does not despise him. But the Cockney thinks of himself as normal and despises those who do not drink and joke as he does. But how friendly and how nice they all were! Perhaps, I thought to myself, Bobby was right after all, and here was another world and an immemorial world—a world indifferent to the false and fleeting values of the town, a world that would still survive and be strong when ephemeral metropolises had passed away and when New Zealanders were already busy at their sketches of St. Paul's.

They tumbled out into the dark with their cheery good-nights.

'Did you hear that postscript by Noel Coward?' came back a voice. 'Wasn't it beautiful?'

X

As I have said, there worked in the room in the Ministry of Information along with George and the Reader in Javanese, a magician. He had practised his art for many years in Sicily, where he had earned a very decent living by casting spells upon such of the Sicilians as might have offended his clients and removing spells by his superior power from members of the wealthier classes. During the days of Italian democracy he had served as a town councillor in the Palermo municipality, being elected as a supporter of the Partito Populare. In the first years after the coming to power of the Fascists he had therefore been somewhat under a cloud. But one day the Fascist Governor was seized with an excruciating stomach-ache shortly after he had trodden upon a toad which the magician kept as a part of his stage property. A democratic past was forgiven and the magician was received back again into full favour. He practised and flourished until the Italian declaration of war, when he was expelled from the country. For he was a British subject, a Jew. His name was Bert. He got a job, as I say, in the Ministry of Information—the fate that is worse than death.

Bert and the Reader in Javanese had made fast friends when Jenkinson, the head of the Patagonian Department in the Ministry, had died one day at his desk next door. Each had discovered the other on tiptoe trying to plant his unanswered minutes in Jenkinson's 'In' tray. For a moment, the Reader in Javanese told me, each fiddled uncertainly with papers, as if he was looking for something. Each tried to pretend that he had got into the wrong room by mistake. Each asked the other if he could do anything for him. Then, in his nervousness, Bert dropped a pencil on the floor. The Reader bent down to pick it up for him, and, like a gun, his two back trouser buttons shot off across the room. The situation was saved.

'Don't you hate it when your trousers come down in a Government department?' said the Reader in Javanese.

'I do not know that it has ever happened to me,' said Bert.

'It has not often happened to me,' said the Reader, 'but, when it does happen, I hate it like hell.'

'But at least let me have the buttons,' said Bert eagerly. 'Bone buttons are invaluable in magic. You've no idea how difficult the times are for magicians. Goat's skin, cock's blood, pig's feet, hemlock—all the properties rationed, and not only rationed, but the price! And now they are even putting toads on points.'

'Is that so?' said the Reader in Javanese. 'Well, by all means have my buttons, if only you can retrieve them from somewhere behind that radiator.'

And he proceeded to fix up his own braces with a Heath Robinson arrangement of safety-pins—a triumph of hope over experience but a small price to pay for the gaining of a friend.

I had never met a magician and I was interested to make the acquaintance of Bert. He used to sit most of the day in an inner room, picking out with one finger his mystic letters on an old and very broken-down typewriter. 'There goes Bert, typewriting away to his Abracadabra,' the Reader in Javanese used to say to George. What he typed no one ever knew, save only the War Cabinet offices, to which he once forwarded by mistake a list of cabbalistic signs in place of a folder on the rice production of Formosa. Whether they ever noticed the difference or not is unknown. The folder came back austerely ticked and minuted, 'For comment, please.'

To the English reader of the twentieth century a claim to magical powers must necessarily seem a mere absurdity, and absurd enough in all conscience Bert in many ways was. But it was in matters irrelevant to his magic—his habits, his dress, his indifference to the generally accepted values of the world—that he was absurd. His beliefs about magic were based on serious evidence and defended with serious logic. If one rejected them, one rejected them *a priori* because one was determined not to admit such explanations of phenomena. The man seemed mad and the conclusions seemed fantastic, but there was a horrible strength about the evidence and a horrible validity in the reasoning. Sometimes one had an awful momentary fear that perhaps in a mad world he alone might prove to be sane—or at the least that the man who believed too much would prove to be wiser than the many who believed too little.

I liked to talk to him on his subject and even sometimes, if opportunity offered, to set him against George. For he, like George, was a rationalist in his faith. He maintained that the evidence in favour of the existence of magical powers was overwhelming. The paths of history upon which he walked were different from those most commonly studied for the School Certificate Examination. So I could not pretend to the reading seriously to check the particular claims that he made. But his general point seemed to me valid. He appealed to *consensus universalis*. He said that people had believed in magic since the beginning of time, that all the greatest of human intellects had accepted it, and that it would therefore be strange indeed if there were not some truth in it. Christianity had, it was true, to some extent controlled it in Europe, but no one who had mixed with the non-European cultures in their native homes could possibly fail to believe in it. It was the sheerest provincialism to deny the existence of magic because you did not notice it in Birmingham.

'The Chinese,' he said, 'mature late. Why, many of them cannot even bilocate till they are twenty-six. But they are an educated nation. With maturity they grow into a belief in magic, not out of it—in much the same way that mature people in England grow out of left-wing opinions.'

'All right,' I asked him one day, 'suppose that we concede, for the sake of argument, that there is some truth in it. But has any good come of it?'

He was delighted at this question, and paid me the compliment of saying that it proved that I was a really intelligent person. He said that most people nowadays had so entirely lost all capacity for weighing evidence in the shaping of their fundamental philosophy that they no longer distinguished between what was true and what they wished to be true. They made up their philosophy to suit their own tastes and said that what they wished to be was. He was indeed delighted to meet someone who could understand that a thing might be true but evil.

'Shakespeare understood it all as well as anyone,' he said to me. 'It's all in *Macbeth*, and if you want it in a modern story then it's in W. W. Jacobs' *Monkey's Paw*. It is possible to obtain the assistance of supernatural power. The proper way to obtain that assistance is through the regular channels—through what Christians call grace—and you can only get the assistance of grace if you pay the moral price. But people can obtain supernatural assistance if they want without paying the moral price, and then they get what they want, but they get it in such a way that it would be better for them that they had not got it. Macbeth became Thane of Cawdor, Thane of Glamis, and King, but it would have been better had he not done so. The old people in Jacobs' story got their money, but only at the expense of their son's death.'

'The crystal-gazer in *John Inglesant* made his customers get into a state of grace before they looked in his crystal,' said George.

'Oh, that was in a novel,' said Bert. 'You can make people do anything in a novel. How much money do you think that there would be in magic if one only sold it to people in a state of grace?'

'But in that case,' I said, 'how do you justify yourself in being a magician?'

'Oh, I'm a professional,' he said. '*Caveat emptor*—I never

asked anybody to use magic. I just sold it to them. It wa no business of mine if some of them came to a bad en any more than it is any business of the wine merchant some of the people who buy his bottles get *deliriu tremens*. Besides, I've got the evil eye, and there's an en of it. If you've got the evil eye and live in Sicily, then yo can't help practising magic if you want to or not.'

'But what about this paying of the moral price?' I aske

'The Sicilians did not want to pay any moral price,' h said. 'The assistance without the moral price is just wha they want.'

'Even though it means coming to a bad end?' I asked.

'Oh, they think they're coming to a bad end anyway,' h said. 'The most that they ask is that they should be abl to bring somebody else to a bad end first. Don't believ those tales about happy pagans. There is always a catch i all the pagan promises—Achilles and the heel, Baldur an the leaf. "There is always a thing forgotten." In all th stories they are always promised immortality and eterna happiness unless some one thing happens, that in genera probability would be very unlikely to happen. But alway from the beginning you know quite well that this on thing is going to happen.'

We had wandered into the main room while this argu ment was going on, and Bert was vaguely manœuvrin about on the floor drawing pentagrams with a piece o chalk.

'For God's sake,' said the Reader in Javanese, 'if you'v this evil eye, why can't you use it on some of the bloke in the Ministry?'

'They're allergic to it,' said Bert. 'One can sink below magic, just like people who never notice anything don't know the names of flowers or birds.'

'That's perfectly true,' said the Reader in Javanese. 'You cannot understand anything worth while except from

ıside. I once killed a man—it was years ago, in Java—
vhen I was still a clergyman.'

He was not very explicit about details, but it was, he
ssured us, 'quite all right' and apparently reflected the
reatest credit on everybody concerned, whether murderer
r murdered.

'You say that murder is wrong,' he explained to us with
ome contempt for our inexperience. 'In a sort of way no
oubt you understand that it is—in the sort of way in
hich a fairly intelligent eunuch could see the wrong in
dultery. But you must pardon me if I find everything that
ou have to say on such a topic unbearably naïve. No one
an know what it is to kill unless they have killed, and no
ne can therefore really know what is wrong in killing un-
ess they have killed. No doubt Bert feels the same about
ıagic.'

'I feel it even more about Jews,' said Bert. 'No one can
nderstand anything who does not understand Jews, and
o one can understand Jews but a Jew. If there is one thing
ıat is absolutely certain in history it is that the Jews are
Chosen People.'

'What exactly do you mean by a Chosen People?' asked
ıe Reader in Javanese.

'It does not matter what exactly I mean,' said Bert. 'We
ill come to that in a moment. But I do claim that it is
vident from history that Jews are entirely different from
ıy other races. If they were not chosen, why have they
ırvived at all? What has happened to all the other races
Old Testament time? They have all gone in the melting-
ot and lost their identity long ago. If the story had been
purely human story, is it not obvious that the Jews
ould have become merged with their neighbours at the
me of the Babylonian Captivity?'

'Ten of the tribes were,' said George.

'Perhaps,' said Bert, 'but I am talking about what is

extraordinary in the story, not what is ordinary. If the
had not been a Chosen People they would have perished i
the Red Sea, they would have perished in Babylon, the
would have perished again after the sack of Jerusalen
They could not possibly have survived the exile of tw
thousand years through the Dark Ages and the Middl
Ages and modern times.'

'They survived,' said the Reader in Javanese, 'becaus
their race was a religion.'

'Who's begging questions now?' said Bert. 'Of cour
they survived because of their religion, but why was the
religion so much stronger than other people's religion
Every other race gave up its distinctive religion when
was no longer convenient to hold it. Why did not th
Jews? The remarkable thing about the Jews is that the
exist—that they have survived at all. This proves them
Chosen People—marked out from all the other people i
the world.'

'That's quite a good argument,' said George, 'but the
many people are different from other people. Christiani
is very different from other religions. Yet you are not
Christian.'

'No,' said Bert, 'but I respect the Christian case—at leas
when it is put forward by rationalists like you. I don
respect the average Christian who cannot give the begi
ning of an account why he is a Christian and is in fa
hardly more intelligent than an intellectual.'

'But why don't you accept the Christian claims, wh
you do accept the Jewish claims?' asked George.

'You know very well why I don't,' said Bert. 'We've be
into all that often before, and it would break the argume
if we went off on it now. My argument of the moment
that the Christian argument is a pretty evenly balanc
argument with pros and cons and difficulties on both sid
and that—oddly enough, so rum is the world—is an a

vantage for you Christians. People expect there to be two sides to a question, and think more of a case if there is something to be said against it. But the Jewish case is utterly different. There there is absolutely nothing to be said against, and so people simply neglect the case just because it is so overwhelming. Have you ever heard anyone give any other explanation of the Jews, good or bad, except that they are a Chosen People?'

'Well, personally, Bert,' said the Reader in Javanese, 'I must frankly confess that I do not like Jews.'

'That has nothing whatsoever to do with it,' said Bert.

'And I rather like them,' said George.

'That has even less to do with it,' he said.

'But, Bert,' I said, 'you aren't an orthodox Jew. You have not got a hat on. You don't eat kosher meat. You come here on Saturday. God knows what you do. You are a Liberal.'

'I am not a Liberal,' said Bert. 'I believe what is proved and do not believe what is not proved. I have lived my life on the Continent. On the Continent a Liberal is a man who hates Christians, just as a Christian is a man who hates Jews. I am no more a Liberal than I am a Christian. I believe that the Jews are the Chosen People. I believe also that a lot of quite sensible regulations were laid down for them when they lived in the desert about three thousand years ago. But I do not think that the Law, particularly the Law as refined and littered and literated by generations of lawgivers, is binding on us in the entirely different circumstances of to-day.'

'But then you are a Liberal,' I persisted.

A shade of real annoyance passed over his face.

'No, I am not a Liberal,' he said. 'A Liberal is a person who believes that the great thing is kindness, and that all religions have a lot of good in them, and that the Jewish religion might as well be kept going in some sort of milk-

and-water way because there it is. I can't tell you how much I don't believe that. I think it the most contemptible, drivelling, whaffling, pass-selling, treacherous apology for a religion that was ever invented.'

'But then what do you believe,' I persisted, 'if you don't believe in the Law and you don't believe in Liberalism?'

He suddenly got up from the floor, where he had been scrawling, drew himself up almost as a soldier to attention, raised his eyes slightly, and said quite simply:

'I believe that Messiah cometh.'

I had had a good deal to do with Jews in my time both socially and in business, but it was typical both of my own shallowness and of the shallowness of the age that it had never occurred to me to show any curiosity about what they believed. Indeed, I had no doubt that most of them, in this no better than Christians, could give but little account of their own beliefs. But I had never fully taken in that there were Jews walking in the London streets in hats and coats, lurking even—God forgive them—in the Ministry of Information, who were still waiting for the coming of Messiah. He walked off, as if towards the inner office, and I thought that he was going to leave us and return to his typewriting. At the last minute he changed his mind and turned round again.

'Can't you see,' he said to me, 'that it is the only truly rational religious faith? The Jews, of course, thought that Messiah was coming, and the deepest of pagan minds, like, for instance, Virgil, thought so too. It is natural for man to think so. It is natural for him, when he looks at the world, to think that some great divine intervention in human history must be destined, or else things do not make sense. How could there be compassion if it were not so?'

'I don't follow,' I said.

'Well, take Browning's Saul,' said Bert. 'David so loved Saul that he was anxious to take on himself some of Saul's suffering. And at first he thinks that in this his love is in a measure superior to the love of God, because Man can suffer for that which he loves, but God, being unlimited, though He can love, cannot suffer. He thinks that God would want to suffer if He could. And then he thinks, How stupid to be talking of what Omnipotent God would do if He could

So wouldst Thou, so wilt Thou.

God will. The divine event in which God will take upon Himself a form in which He can suffer must be coming.'

'But this seems to me all an argument for Christianity,' I said, 'not for Judaism.'

'No,' said Bert, 'it is an argument for Messiah—an exposition why intelligent people expected him to come. And so, when Christ came, it was not unnatural that He should have been hailed as Messiah, just because He was expected. But, with all respect to George, I am afraid that I cannot admit Christ's claim to be Messiah. The Christian Higher Criticism has proved the case for Judaism. It has proved that Christ was not Messiah, while leaving quite unshaken the case that Messiah cometh. Oh, I know all the ups and downs of the argument. Still, in the last analysis I do not admit the claim, and I do not admit it for this reason: I think that, if Messiah had really come, then there would have been a vastly greater difference between the pre-Messianic and the post-Messianic world. There does not seem to me to be any such enormous difference. Men seem to me to have been much of a muchness, part good, part bad, both before and after the Incarnation.'

'Oh, but surely there is a good deal of difference,' I objected. 'Christianity has achieved a number of things that no non-Christian civilisation has achieved.'

'Oh yes, a number of things,' he admitted. 'Christ has had His influence—I'm not denying that. But has His influence been such that there is any reason to imagine that His power was supernatural? Aristotle has had a lot of influence, and Karl Marx, and Julius Cæsar, and Confucius, but no one ever imagined that they were gods.'

'But what sort of influence would you expect Him to have?' asked George.

'Well, if it was really true that those who took the Christian Sacraments received the grace of God in a quite special sense denied to the rest of us—if it was really true, as He promised, that wherever two or three were gathered together in His name He was in the midst of them, then—well, I don't exactly know what I should expect, but I do know that I should expect something pretty considerable. Why aren't Christians more different? That they are not shows, to my mind, that the rational belief is that Messiah is promised but that He has not yet come.'

This was his faith. As a Jew and as a humane man—and he was reasonably humane—he naturally detested Hitler's persecution of his co-religionists, but he always insisted that Hitler had done 'good to the Jews on the whole.' Hitler was, of course, 'a sort of anti-Semite,' but his anti-Semitism was less dangerous, if more offensive, than that of the secularist, particularly if the secularist was a Jew who maintained that Jew was no different from Gentile. 'He has not wanted to do good. He's a devil, but, like most devils, he's a reasonably good theologian. One always finds that devils are—far better on the whole than men. What really matters is that Jews should be recognised as different from other people. It is, of course, practically inconvenient if they are thus recognised only by being persecuted. But it is far better for them to be persecuted than to be treated as if they were just a sort of Christian. That is the supreme insult and the supreme blasphemy. The nineteenth century was the most dangerous century in all Jewish history. Jews were fast losing their faith under toleration, but once you start persecuting the Jews you arouse all their racial pride. Hitler has saved us.'

'That's one way of putting it,' said the Reader in Javanese, 'but if what you really fear is peace and tolerance, are not you afraid of victory? They all tell us that the post-war world is going to be more peaceful, more glorious, more free from fear even than the nineteenth century. Aren't you afraid of that?'

'Not a bit,' said Bert cheerfully. 'Not a little bit. That's the great comfort of this war over the last. Nobody really believes in the Rosy Dawn that's coming this time. Just think of our history,' he said, 'just think of it.'

He staggered a little almost as if he were a drunken man, and started again to walk towards the inner room. On its threshold he again turned and, drawing himself up to his full height and raising his hand, said with all solemnity:

'God spoke to our father Abraham, and Abraham begat Isaac, and Isaac begat Jacob and Jacob begat Joseph. We were held in captivity in Egypt, and thence Moses led us out by the Red Sea. We wandered for forty years in the wilderness until we inherited the Promised Land. The Judges ruled us, and then the Kings ruled us, David and those that came after him. We were taken into captivity into Babylon, but we came back—the two of our tribes. The Seleucids came, and we fought them. The Romans came, and we were scattered over the face of the earth, eternal wanderers, with no home anywhere. Any other race than the Divine race would have perished thus. Where to-day are the Moabites or the Edomites, the Philistines or the Amalekites? But we of Israel, we did not perish. We did not perish because we are from God and we wait the appointed hour, the hour when Messiah cometh. What fool can think that a little touch of persecution can kill us —we who were old when Pharaoh and Nebuchadnezzar,

Cæsar and Herod were unknown and who still live when Cæsar and Pharaoh are mouldered to the dust. God of Abraham, how proud I am to be a Jew! How I despise Jews who are not proud to be Jews!

> Thou, if Thou wast He, Who at mid-watch came
> By the starlight, naming a dubious name.

I was fascinated, but the Reader in Javanese, to whom it was clearly a familiar turn, had been quietly telephoning while it was going on. He now put down the receiver.

'Thompson's dead,' he said dramatically.

'Dead,' said Bert. 'In his room?'

'I think not,' said the Reader in Javanese. 'But, anyway, the room's empty now.'

'Quick, the files,' said Bert.

George had not taken as much part as was his custom in the conversation, and as we walked away together from the Ministry to lunch, leaving Bert and the Reader in Javanese still at it, I asked him why.

'Oh, well,' he said, 'it's not as new to me as it was to you. I've heard all that Bert has to say and had it out with him a number of times. One can't have it all out from A to Z every day. Life's too short.'

'He's one of those people who says quite sensible things,' I said, 'but gives the impression that he says them because they are surprising and not because he really believes them.'

'Oh, I don't know that that's fair,' said George. 'I think that he's perfectly genuine in all his Jewish religion stuff, and there's obviously quite a reasonable case for it. It's certainly a great deal more intelligent than common agnosticism, and he's annoyed when he comes across intelligent Jews who abandoned Jewish beliefs for secular beliefs. He thinks that that really is stepping out of the light. I have nothing against him there.'

'But he can't really believe in all that stuff about magic?' I said.

'Oh, I think that he believes that all right,' said George, 'and, what's more, I believe it up to a point. That is to say, I do not know that I believe in all the details of his abracadabra, but I believe that something happens and that there are ways of getting into touch with preternatural powers.'

'It may be all right in Sicily,' I said, 'but do you really think that you are going to get people to believe in that in England?'

'I should have thought that they would believe anything,' said George. 'Any fortune-teller can make a fortune these days. Supposing that people learnt that there really were a lot of rum things that do take a lot of explaining away? My fear is that, for twopence, if it got put across with at all a competent propaganda, they would believe a great deal too much.'

'Yes,' I said, 'Bert does not seem a bad fellow, but there is something sort of indoors about him—a sort of atmosphere of never having played any game.'

'Good heavens,' said George, 'what an extraordinary thing to say! I should not imagine that he had ever dreamed of playing one.'

'When we were at school,' I said, 'they always used to say to us, "Of course, it's all very well making all this fuss about games now. But when you grow up you will find that it's brains that matter, and the little swots that you kick round the place now will steal all the good jobs from you." But I must say that I have not found that at all. Of course, brains matter in the sense that being right matters. But it's been my experience that the capacity to put your head down in a loose bully is much more likely to bring you out right than the capacity to get a distinction in trials.'

'There's a great danger in being too good at games,' said George, 'and living on your athletic reputation.'

'Oh yes, granted,' I agreed. 'But, short of that, games give a kind of balance to your judgment. People say, What can it matter forty years from now whether you got that rouge or not? with the implication that all the things that you bother about when you are grown up will all matter enormously. But it seems to me the great beauty of games is that you can get frightfully keen on them, though even a schoolboy can see that the results of them do not really matter. And when you're middle-aged and begin to discover that the world is not really as important as all that and that there is no great sense in getting to the top of the tree and that the glittering prizes only seemed glittering so long as one had not quite outgrown one's adolescence—well, you're thankful if you've learnt to do things decently even when you could not see that they were very important. Take a chap like Bobby. His reasons were sometimes good and sometimes bad, but he had a kind of instinct which came from out of doors that warned him off the roads that were bad. Now I dare say that Bert's a good fellow and he will always give excellent reasons for doing what he is going to do. But I do not feel that he has that balance of normality against which to check his decisions.'

'There's a good deal in all this, Peter,' said George, 'but I'm surprised to hear it from you with your parlour Bolshevism. You will be telling me that the Battle of Waterloo was won on the playing-fields of Eton next.'

'That's the awful thing about clichés,' I said. 'So many of them are true. One fights hard not to say them for very shame's sake, but some time in later middle age they all come tumbling out one after the other. You see, George, that is the devil. I do know the difference between right and wrong.'

'Of course,' said George, 'but can you remember which is

which? That is what so many people find so difficult these days.'

We pushed through the swing doors to lunch.

XI

To the grown-up a war is just a slice out of life. One may be an older man at the end of it than at the beginning, but, if so, one ascribes one's ageing to trouble and anxiety rather than to the passage of years. Four or five years more are not reckoned to make a difference in kind to one's age in the late thirties or early forties. But among the young it is different. There every passing year makes so wholly a new person that the boy or girl who has grown up during the war seems to be almost a creature of the war with no existence apart from it and not one whose normal life has been interrupted by the coming of war. Thus my own two younger children began their schooling during these years. They learnt to read in a world in which the war was the only thing to read about. The world of rations and casualties and air raids was to them the normal world. They spoke with awe, as if they had met Methuselah at tea, of a neighbour slightly their senior, 'Jennie Thessiger, who remembers when there wasn't a war.' To them there was no other world—no knowledge of a world when children lived in their own homes and with their own parents, of those legendary creatures of a Saturnian age who had mothers who had not been killed in air raids. Because children can solve the immediate problems of life even in these strange circumstances, can laugh and eat and play, can make a bathing-pool out of the crater of a bomb-hole, can clamour for an expedition to see a wrecked aircraft, where men were burnt to death, much as their elders had clamoured to be taken to the pantomime, therefore we easily tell one another that the human race is, as George put it, 'infinitely adjustable.' It is but a half-truth. There is a vast price in abnormality of psychology to be paid for all this abnormality of experience. We excuse the blunders of the policies of the years between the wars by explaining that the world lacked leaders because a generation was blotted out. But the problem was not really a problem of quantity but of quality. It was not merely that many were dead but that those who survived were abnormal. It was not that some were physically dead but that more were spiritually dead.

One thinks of the Bright Young People of the twenties, *quorum*, to my shame to some extent, if not *pars magna,* at least *pars fui.* What can we say of ourselves as we look back? What can we say except that we were not properly and fully speaking human beings? Of qualities the possession of which makes man to be man we had hardly so much as heard. It was not merely that we were unchaste and arrogant, ill-mannered and dishonourable, but rather that we hardly knew the meaning of such great words as chastity or humility, honour or courtesy. Indeed, we did not know their meaning in any real sense. If we had read of them at all, we had read of them only in some silly, jeering modern book, where the writer knew only of these virtues as negatives and had not ever learnt that they were positives. We valued cleverness and—God save the mark, for that is the extraordinary thing as I look back upon it—we thought that we were clever. It was so brazen as to be almost in a way admirable, a feat in impudence, that such creatures as we should have dared to be proud. As I look back upon those years they seem to me to bear all the marks of a ghastly and transcendental fable—clever young boys and girls sitting round and discussing how they were descended from monkeys and none of them noticing that in their habits, in their environment, even in a measure in their features, they were every day more visibly descending into monkeys.

Ruth's family was, of course, a little older than mine, and therefore the changes of the war had a different impact on it than on mine. Robert, the youngest, was eleven when the war came, and therefore by 1943 had reached fifteen. The war—superficially at any rate—affected children of such an age less than it did either their elders or their youngers. Living in the country both at home and at school, he did not see enough of air raids for them to have any important nervous effect on him. The nation's feeding throughout the war was ably managed, and there was no reason to think that youth was a permanent sufferer from either the quality or the quantity of food. On the other hand, the early teens are years when larger interests have not yet developed. Robert's interest in the war and the world was passing and superficial. The results of battles were to him very much like the results of football matches, only obviously less interesting because more distant and because seeing alone is believing and one did not see the players in action. No one but a fool would complain of this. I would much rather any day have young Robert shouting for his pony, with his open shirt and a dirty lumber-jacket, than I would have the odious little prigs in their Youth Parliaments, passing resolutions complaining of their parents and demanding the incarceration of their Fascist grandmothers as enemies of the people. Of all virtues the root is humility, and the pleasures of the body are given to us because we can delight in them without being in danger of spiritual pride.

Robert was an out-of-doors boy, as, indeed, were all the Fossetts, but he was not by any means a fool. Indeed, he was good at his books and, whatever troubles the future might hold before him, at fifteen he gave promise of a better brain than Martin's and none of Martin's difficult temperament. In reaction against the absurdities and charlatanry of Martin's headmaster, I had persuaded Ruth to be hung for a sheep as soon as a lamb and to let Robert go to Eton. We had clubbed together and somehow managed to find the money. I had made Tony give lunch to a friend of his in the Ministry of Supply, and through his influence the Government had been induced to pay up its compensation for the perambulator canopies. Ruth, like many other people, who thought themselves threatened with bankruptcy at the beginning of the war, found herself after four years of it better off than she had expected. Even Uncle Dotty had been moved for the first time in his life to be a little helpful.

There were of course those who asked, as did some of my friends of the Society for Rearranging the Poor, why a boy should have special opportunities in life simply because of the accident of his birth. In theory I might have asked such a question myself. But, faced with the reality of a practical decision, I could but answer by challenging anyone to give a better reason why a boy should be given some special training in life than that he was a son of Robert Fossett. Such paternity created a far greater probability that he would benefit by such a special training than any accident of high marks in an examination.

'Boys,' said Bert one day, 'should be taught something practical—something that will help them to make a living and also be of some practical use in the world. Not too much of these old dead languages.'

'Such as what?' I asked. 'Book-keeping? Basic English?'

'No,' he said, 'neither book-keeping nor basic English. If I had my way I would teach them astrology, just enough Latin so that they can get the incantations right and read Paracelsus in the original, but apart from that pure astrology. It's practical—astrological journalism is the best-paid journalism on the market to-day—and it's educational because you can't understand history except through astrology, and, what's more, it broadens the mind. I would teach them astrology and beat them until they bleed if they won't learn it. That's my idea of education.'

But this opinion was an eccentricity. Most people these days have, I find, no views on education *per se*. Educational policy is to-day to most people simply a counter in the chess game of politics. It is no longer pretended that it is a disadvantage to a boy to learn Latin and Greek. It is admitted to be an advantage but asked why some should have this privilege at the expense of others. 'If my Johnny is not to learn Greek, then why should the lord's son learn it?' Most of the so-called educational schemes to-day are really schemes for the abolition of education. But Eton, whether it be through her arrogance, her traditions or her wealth, whether it be through her virtue or in a measure through her vices, has at any rate risen superior to these advertising cheapjacks and the pressure of the politician. There in superb disdain all tastes are catered for and even those who want to be educated are not actively discouraged.

Perhaps it was because when I went down to Eton I saw him dressed in the familiar tails and white tie and turn-down collar in which I had first known his father thirty years before that I persuaded myself that there was more of his father in Robert than in either of the other children. But I think, in truth, that it was so. I think that there was very much of an echo of his father in the unfledged excitement with which he bubbled over at his first lessons in Greek. To the boy who has the music of it at all in him there is a tremendous adventure in the Greek letters. The achievement of them is a sort of intellectual puberty. At fifteen the stories and the love of Greek literature lay ahead still, but Greek was already his 'favourite suubject.'

'I'm up to an awfully funny man, Uncle Peter,' he told

me one day through a muffin. 'He's called Pilkington, and he set us a Greek grammar paper. We had to give the principal parts of a lot of verbs, and along with the rest was one called Sago.'

'Sago?' I said, hastily trying to recall my all-too-rusty learning.

'No,' said Robert. 'When he came to give the paper back, he said, "I'm afraid that this is a highly irregular verb. The principal parts are Sago-Riso-Tetapioca-Esemelina. Perhaps it was hardly a fair question."'

The jests of pedagogy!

Margaret had got to eighteen by 1943. The war had an effect on her almost the opposite to that which it had on Robert. It had largely passed Robert by, but Margaret, a girl and three years older, had all the conventional desire to 'get into it.' In a way this was, in her, a slightly absurd desire. It was perhaps right and desirable that at school she showed no liking for book learning. A little learning in women is a very dangerous thing and a lot of learning by obvious simple arithmetic more dangerous still. Girls' schools in these days are much too indiscriminate in encouraging it. Ruth and I had been a little careful to choose for her a school where she would get companionship without any danger of becoming a blue stocking, and in that we succeeded. She left school early—indeed, not to put too fine a point on it, she was expelled—expelled, it is true, in a most ladylike way and with the highest expressions of esteem on both sides, but the nuns very reasonably said that, if Margaret absolutely refused to pay any attention to their rules about the visiting of other girls' rooms, they could not be responsible for her continuance in the school. Margaret, with all generosity, said that she entirely saw their point of view.

Although there were certain practical inconveniences in expulsion, yet neither her mother nor I held it very seriously against her. After all, if one cannot be expelled from a girls' school, what can one be expelled from? But what was perhaps a little silly was her subsequent behaviour. A creature of a farm, Margaret was never truly at home unless she was wading through the muck in her Wellingtons or perched up on the driver's seat at harvest-time, crying 'Whoa' and 'Go on' at the poor fly-plagued, sweating horses. 'I have never known a girl who had the land more naturally and more fully in her blood than she. Her furrow was from her earliest teens as straight as another's die. Margaret ought to settle down on the farm, and, when the time comes, marry a horse,' said her mother, perhaps a little ungallantly.

With such tastes and with the needs of the nation as they were, it was clear that, if she wished to serve, her best service would be to help her mother on the farm. But somehow that would not do. There was a restlessness in her, and she must get away from home and do something different and unfamiliar, something that was an adventure. 'La donna é mobile,' I comforted Ruth when Margaret babbled about a job in the Transport Corps. To what strange ends this longing for adventure often leads us! It led Margaret to a dim job as a filing clerk in one of the dullest of Whitehall's Government departments. There she sat from nine o'clock until six, six days a week, putting pieces of paper in boxes, seeing that the inconvenient ones were lost, talking on the telephone, drinking vast quantities of tea, eating vast quantities of cake, looking out always on the same blank stretch of wall, eating always at the same hour the same food and at the same canteen. A life less adventurous it would be hard to conceive. A night spent sitting up with a lambing ewe was in comparison with this a magic casement of romance, a fairy tale touching upon all the mysteries of life and death. Even had the policies of her masters been of the last moment of importance, her part in them would have been equally monotonous and a routine. Yet, as far as I could judge, the policies were policies of a shattering futility. Even the War Office seemed to have more connection with the war. The whole sub-department could have been easily closed down without the least loss to the nation or indeed difference to anybody. It was one of those departments of which Whitehall has so many, whose masters deck themselves out with pomposity in order to conceal from themselves and from the world the utter emptiness of their lives. Indeed, there was only one thing to be said for her monotonous life, and that was that Michael Paravane shared it.

Michael, a gallant soldier, wounded and invalided from the army, was a Cuthbert *malgré lui.* He worked in the Ministry under protest and, because that was the best that his battered body could do, serving the Other Liberal as a private secretary. He was not in the same room as Margaret, but there was, as far as I could gather, a good deal of legitimate cause for communication between his room and hers—so much cause that there was from the one room to the other a private telephone line with no exchange to go through and a private handle. And such a line with private handle to twiddle and not too much to do is a sovereign recipe for trouble. A private telephone line is a very faithful instrument for preliminary romantic reconnaissances, having all the advantages of intimacy and none of the dangers of contiguity. There were, I gather, what the character in Ben Travers' play calls 'goings-on'—nothing at all reprehensible, of course, but prolonged telephone calls and private jokes and tea and buns at odd hours and off duty no end of 'Michael says' and 'Margaret says' and embarrassingly exact knowledge by each when the other would be on duty. Michael had an engagingly naïve habit of transferring his private hopes and fears into general opinions. When I heard him argue for the national importance of early marriages I knew that there was danger. When I heard him maintain that the deepest and most philosophic line in Shakespeare was 'In delay there lies no plenty' I knew that all was lost.

One day he broached to me his ambitions.

'As far as I am concerned, Michael,' I said, 'which, to tell the truth, is not very far, there is no one in all the world whom I would rather have for a nephew-in-law than you. But has Margaret any opinions on the matter—to say nothing of her mother?'

'Oh, Margaret's agreeable,' said Michael. 'She says that if I don't keep her she will have to earn her own living, and she would sooner marry than earn.'

'How almost Pauline!' I said. 'And what does Ruth say?'

'She's nothing against it,' said Michael, 'but she says that Margaret's a bit young.'

'Well, that seems to me not unreasonable, I must say, Michael,' I said. 'I am all for early marriages, and I think that a marriage is all the more likely to succeed if there is a reasonable degree of risk in it. But still, eighteen is a bit young for a girl to commit herself for life. If you're going to go all Shakespearean, then go right through with him. "Sweet and twenty" was his formula, and people matured a bit earlier then than they do to-day.'

'But I'm more than twenty,' said Michael. 'It's a bit tough on me to have to do the waiting.'

'Well, you've something to wait for now,' I said.

And so it was agreed for the time—that there should, if they wished, be a non-committal unofficial engagement between Michael and Margaret and that all should be reconsidered and, if agreed, put on a regular footing when Margaret was twenty.

XII

MARTIN, as we have seen, the war had found a schoolboy and already a most admirable cricketer. He was a rugby footballer, too, of very much more than average merit—a strong-running wing three-quarter. I visited him at Trumpinghurst during the blitz and the Michaelmas term of 1940 and saw him play in their match against Clifton. I always love the atmosphere of schools, the timelessness of the conversations of common-rooms, the eternal complaints that the prefects are not pulling their weight, that the algebra is not what it was, and that forwards no longer get their heads down in the scrum as they used to do. At half a hundred beloved places in England it is going on every Saturday afternoon of the autumn months round toast and tea and a blazing fire, differing from place to place only in the names of the delinquents. Fools sneer at schoolmasters, calling them boys among men and men among boys, and indeed theirs is a different world from that of stockbrokers and politicians, but he would be a brazen judge who felt certain that it was not a better one. In this autumn of 1940, with its nightly raids on London, it was a recreation, even if one also felt that it was something of a voyage into unreality, to come down into a life where boys prattled still without self-consciousness of strong and weak three-quarters and of a great kick from the goal-line which found touch just beyond the half-way flag-post.

It was a fine open match on a hard, dry field under a bright October sun. Trumpinghurst were behind most of the game, but in the last five minutes the ball came out of the scrum in mid-field, and a grand run by the three-quarters took it right down the field. Martin on the left wing got the ball with only the full back between him and the line. He sold the full back a lovely dummy in reverse and grounded just by the touch-line. The boys pressed forward on to the ropes until one of them burst and a batchful was precipitated forwards on to the grass. A cry went up, 'He's over.' An apoplectic housemaster went so red in the face with his cheering that I expected dissolution. Up ran the little referee, and for a breathless, silent moment examined the scene. Then we saw the Cliftonians drifting back towards the goal and Trumpinghurst trooping out to mid-field for the kick to be taken. He had allowed it. How we cheered! The angle for the kick was too acute. Yet it did not matter. The try alone made the score six-five to Trumpinghurst, and all was well.

Yet cricket was his real game. He was captain of the eleven at school in the summer of 1941, and I got down to Trumpinghurst to see the Marlborough match that June. Martin played a grand innings—an innings which showed that he had the makings in him of a truly first-class bat, if only the times were such that first-class bats could be made in them. It was more than a triumph of batsmanship; it was also a triumph of character. Trumpinghurst had a hundred and thirty-seven to get in their final innings, and six wickets were down for eighty-three. All the good bats except Martin were out, and Nos. 9, 10 and 11 of the team of a small school are usually very uncertain performers. Martin bestrode the game like a veteran. He curbed his naturally free style, ran no risk at all, played maiden overs, while the school sat round in agonising suspense. Then at last a bowler grew tired and bowled loose. Martin seized his opportunity, seeing that with the inevitable change of bowling it must be taken 'now or never.' He opened out his shoulders and helped himself to four lovely fours off successive balls. The sixteen runs changed the chance of the game. Naturally and rightly he took all the bowling that he could for himself—firmly dominated the shivering rabbits at the other end—cautioned them, sent them back several times when they called in their nervousness for foolish runs, and at last, with a gratifying lack of sentimentality and false chivalry, unhesitatingly sacrificed the wicket of one of them when he tried to run for a hit that was lodged clean in cover point's hands. 'I'm not coming,' he shouted and remained firmly in his crease. The rabbit was run out by yards.

The ninth wicket fell at a hundred and thirty-three. It is one of the great paradoxes of cricket that, when there is a really close and exciting finish, it falls in the nature of things on the weakest batsman to bear this greatest responsibility. I remember now that shaking, ambling Alp of a boy dragging himself out to the wicket. He was not a bad fast-medium bowler, I believe, with a nasty bit of a swerve, but his one notion of batting was to lash out madly—to count himself lucky if he got one six, knowing that there could never be any hope of repetition. One six would have been enough this afternoon, but the risk was too great. Martin met him as he came out and clearly told him not to attempt it, but instead to keep his bat firmly in the block. There were five balls to go for over, and the Alp was an obedient pupil. There was indeed 'a breathless hush in the Close to-night.' The agonies of cricket, because they are rarer, are therefore keener than those of any other game. There cannot have been one of us round the ground who did not count the balls. The Alp blocked three. Then there was one to leg, which he had but to touch and it must have gone for four, but he was too nervous even to attempt to do so. The last ball he popped up dangerously in the air and half-way down the pitch, but no hand got to it. It was over. Martin received. He played one ball, and then off the second flicked a most lovely wristy cut. It flashed past third man and to the boundary and all was over. The match was won.

Martin had only made sixty-two not out, but it was an

innings which showed indubitably that he had first-class cricket in him. It was in every way worthy of his father—indeed, in some ways more than worthy of him. For Martin showed himself to possess in embryo all Bobby's free and gracious flashing strokes. But he also showed himself to be a master of restraint in crisis—a rare accomplishment at seventeen, an accomplishment that Bobby with his nervous, impatient temperament never quite acquired. He was chosen to play for the Rest against the Lords' Schools at the end of the term, but fortune was not with him. He played three balls, but then, coming out to drive the fourth, missed it and was bowled. But even four balls were enough to wring a tribute out of an old salt in the pavilion. 'Pity,' said the old salt, 'that young fellow looked as if he had some cricket in him.'

Yet the purely moral virtues of the straight bat are sometimes exaggerated. It cannot be pretended that everything about him during these years was as admirable as his athletics. Keats has a very true passage in his preface to *Endymion*. 'The imagination of a boy,' Keats writes, 'is healthy, and the mature imagination of a man is healthy; but there is a space of life between, in which the soul is in a ferment, the character undecided, the way of life uncertain, the ambitions thick-sighted; thence proceed mawkishness and all the thousand bitters which those men I speak of have necessarily tasted.' With the happiest of fortune there are few so well balanced that they can pass through this 'space of life between' wholly without faltering. It was Martin's fate to be called on to pass through it in a time of the unhappiest fortune. The death of his father had driven him in on himself, given him a sense of grievance against life—a grievance that he could not himself wholly understand. He aired it in rebellion at school—not the rebellion of healthy, unmalicious rule-breaking, but a rebellion that tended a little towards bitterness and sterility and a delight in being difficult. Psycho-analysis was the sovereign remedy for all problems of Brakesmith, Martin's headmaster. Adding incest to injury with patient care, he totted up the score of a boy's pre-natal handicaps. Should his Latin prose abound with false concords, should his slow leg-breaks be of erratic length, should he cease to believe in God or come to believe in Him inordinately, should he be impertinent to his housemaster or fall in love with the matron, Brakesmith recommended with unfaltering monotony that he be psycho-analysed. 'As good as Confirmation,' he said, 'and, if you can afford it, no reason why he shouldn't have a second innings.'

Naturally this insane hobby only pandered to Martin's belief that he was a 'special case.'

It is usually unwise to allow a boy to linger on for long at school after his school ambitions have been achieved. Boys are not good at resting on laurels, and all too often he who tries lazily to repeat triumphs already gained fails to do so and ends outdistanced by those who had previously been his inferiors. Certainly it would have been a mistake to have kept Martin on at Trumpinghurst after he had had his term as captain of the eleven. Yet there were still four months to be filled in before he could join up. What could we do with him?

The Reader in Javanese assured me that Oxford had improved during the war. All that he meant, of course, was that there were fewer undergraduates and that even the ranks of his colleagues had been somewhat thinned out by the demands of national service. High-table, protected by ample screens from the territory below the salt, was beginning to take upon itself something of the blessed nature of a private dining-room. He had never spoken to an undergraduate since I had gone down. The experiment, once made, was never to be repeated. The merits of a university were assessed by him entirely by the absence of undergraduates, and, since it caused a diminution in their numbers, a world war was unreservedly to be welcomed. It is true that when the undergraduates went out from his college a number of A.T.S. came in to take their places. It might have been expected that the Reader would have thought the exchange to be no advantage. But in refuge from his unfortunate experience with one coloured lady he had in old age ceased to count women as human beings. They were so far below him that their invasion could not even be seriously resented. It was as if one said that earwigs were more plentiful this year. Had I fully understood the bases of his judgments at the time, I should not perhaps have been greatly moved by them to send Martin to Oxford. It was, as it proved, a foolish step. The Reader's only anxiety was that it be made absolutely clear that nothing in the long-standing friendship with the uncle should involve him in having to see the nephew when he went down to Oxford for his week-ends. To this I readily agreed. I did not think that Martin would derive either edification or amusement from his company, and—to be quite honest—I was not sufficiently proud of the association to wish the incidents of it to be displayed before the irreverent young. Besides, he was usually in London at the Ministry of Information.

The life of an undergraduate in war-time Oxford is a dismal fate. The little victims play all too regardful of their doom. When I was up in the 20's I knew a Siamese prince, who explained to his tutor that it was a national custom that all younger sons of the royal house be trampled to death by elephants at the age of twenty-one. That being so, he really could not feel that it was of great moment whether he got a third or a fourth in his final schools. Much the same, if it be not too brutal a thought, must be the feelings of war-time undergraduates.

No one suffers more in character during war-time than

those who are not yet quite old enough for it. Waiting inactive for the great adventure is a very invitation to demoralisation. Most people are pretty foolish when they are undergraduates, and I doubt if there was ever anyone who was more foolish than I. It is not for me, therefore, to sit in judgment of avuncular priggishness. The conversation of Martin and his friends was, I dare say, no more idiotic than had been the conversation of myself and my friends twenty years before. It was not for me to condemn when they displayed an absurd mastery of the jargon of sexual perversion and at the same time a complete ignorance of the date of the Battle of Waterloo, the difference between Bach and Beethoven or Murillo and Michelangelo or the name of the final school which they were supposed to be studying. That is what undergraduates are. The only question is whether they should be in war-time. There seemed an added absurdity in such folly beneath the looming shadow of Armageddon—prattling about *Lady Chatterley's Lover* while the Japanese were marching into Singapore.

It seems ungenerous to write like this of boys who in a few years were to face the test of courage and to prove themselves in it—of many who, 'following a falling star,' have left their bones on the Atlantic sea-bed or desert sands or in a burning bomber. Yet it is fatuous to write if one does not write the truth, and I must record as truth that, though the men were to prove better than I, the boys were frankly unattractive. Naturally enough, as is the habit of such persons, these young men expressed in their conversation a complete contempt for all traditional systems of religion and morals. Martin certainly abandoned at that time the practice of religion to which he had been brought up. It was hardly for me with my own record to be shocked at that, and the college chaplain, who might have been expected to mind, airily dismissed his agnosticism with the reflection 'All the young men give up religion at eighteen, but they all return to it at twenty-three'—a most comfortable discovery for one who had devoted his entire adult life to ministering to undergraduates.

Into what degree of practice either Martin or his friends may have carried their professed moral or immoral principles I did not think it my business to inquire. Even had it been my business and even had I been possessed of the full dossier of their achievements, I doubt if a direct frontal attack on the details of their conduct would have been the best approach to them. The root fault of these young men was not this or that positive sin, but their lack of charity. Piers Plowman has told us that

> 'Chastity without charity shall be chained in hell.
> It is as lifeless as a light whose lamp is out.

This is not a plea against chastity; it is a plea for charity, without which no virtue is a virtue. And with these young men, too, little purpose would have been served by obtaining a formal obedience to the law if the root fault was left untouched. It was there that the remedy was needed.

With Martin, at any rate, 'the space between' was soon crossed and the other side was safely reached. Most youths sow a few oats, wild or Quaker, of moral disorder or political extravagance, as the case may be, but those who have been brought up firmly in the traditions usually return. Few apostatise save through their parents' fault. The military discipline of the Army soon shook Martin back, and it was some years before the statutory twenty-three when, to the unconcealed shock of the chaplain, Martin, on a visit to Oxford, presented himself in the college chapel for Holy Communion. 'Very satisfactory, but a trifle—well, shall we say a trifle premature?' muttered the good old man.

Bobby always used to say that life was very difficult for a young man who was good-looking and good at games and at all else in which excellence in youth is admired if he should also be in all respects too effortlessly continent. It was then hard indeed for him not to feel a contempt of superiority for those weaker brethren who could not sail so unruffled through all the problems of life. It was good for the young to learn that they were vulnerable through a fall. I suppose that it was something like this that St. Augustine meant when he said that *etiam peccata* might be useful in leading us to the greater knowledge of God, or Mariana in *Measure for Measure* when she tells us:

> They say best men are moulded out of faults
> And for the most become much more the better
> For being a little bad.

So I think that Martin was less hard for having been for a time a little foolish, for having learnt that he was not wholly stronger than others. I hope that I do not think so only because I so badly need this plea in mitigation in order to make any sort of excuse for my own youth.

The exact immediate quality of Martin's recovered Christianity I really cannot estimate. There is, of course, a degree of truth in saying that all Christians have to accept the same creed and the same facts, but for all that there is a world of difference between Christians. I do not refer to the difference between sect and sect or between school and school, important and real as these differences are. I mean the differences in the degree of perception of different people. It is like Turner and the lady and the number of colours that they could see in the sunset. Holding the same beliefs, we differ from one another in what we can see in those beliefs. Wherever I have found myself agreeing with George I have also found that George saw much more in the belief than I had ever seen, and learnt more from an agreement with him than I would from a conversion by another.

So there are differences in the quality of belief, and as a

general rule, except among the rarest and most remarkable of souls, the quality of a young man's belief is not apt to be a deep one. He is still filled with the novelty of life, and the proposition that this world is sufficient to itself does not yet seem to him absurd. Death is not yet a reality, and for all practical purposes he thinks of himself as immortal. If Death has come into his life at all, he resents it as an abnormality, an outrage and an intrusion. Such intrusion is different from the Christian attitude, to which Death is a familiar. Thus it is not uncommon among the young that they come to believe Christianity to be true for some time before they believe it to be relevant. I remember Bobby telling me that he thought that his own attitude could be fairly thus described for some years during his middle twenties. Thus he had come to accept the metaphysical case for God and the historical case for Christianity, but somehow he still thought that all the practical problems of every day could be settled on their intrinsic merits—'as if,' he said later when describing this phase, 'they had really intrinsic merits.' It may be that the son in his turn passed through something of the same phase as the father, but, if so, he passed through it, if anything, I think, more rapidly.

Martin had landed in Egypt in October of 1942, just about the same time as the Allied forces were landing at the other end of the African coast. He was with the Eighth Army throughout the last months of its African campaigning. I had a number of letters from him during those months—little informative as such letters must necessarily be—and heard much of him from a couple of fellow-officers who were invalided back to England at about the turn of the year. They called on me and I entertained them, and it was obvious from their conversation that they had taken Martin to their hearts. In the adventure of war he had quite thrown off the last of those difficult moods which he had to some extent carried away with him from his schooldays. He was fascinated by 'the delicious corruption of Egypt.' 'Egypt,' he wrote to me, 'was invented to make Swinburne seem funny. After one has talked with an Egyptian dragoman it is not very easy to believe in "Glory to Man in the highest, Man is the master of things." If there is no such thing as Original Sin, then I suppose that Egyptian dragomen were immaculately conceived, and to believe that is more difficult by a long chalk than belief in the most difficult of the Christian mysteries.'

Yet this was but a passing cynicism, the casual verdict on two days in Cairo. His journey was to the west and to the battlefront—for the last stage of the advance up from El Alamein to the Mareth and, as he hoped, to Tunis and Bizerta. He brought to war—so his fellow-officers told me—an almost Elizabethan gaiety. He greeted the adventure of battle with gigantic laughter, and its discomforts as further fuel to the fun. His fellow-officers, who were older and more set in their ways, minded the discomforts and were even too old to tell the lie that they were not afraid. They could not quite understand Martin's gaiety, even though they were grateful for it. I am not quite sure that I could quite understand it myself. It was entirely unconnected with any belief in the causes for which we were fighting. To English politics he was indifferent, though even his cynicism was not quite proof against disapproval of the antics of the French. The Italians he liked because he found their incompetence childlike and charming. The Germans he respected as efficient soldiers and showed an absurdly excessive scepticism in disbelieving tales of their atrocities.

These opinions, which I recite, are obviously as opinions neither valuable, true nor important. They are obviously but the immaturities of a boy in the twenties, thrown into a man's part before he had reached the mental stature of a man. He had developed a certain talent for minor verse which, derivative and Housmanic as it obviously was, yet gave a not ungraceful expression to his lack of political faith and his belief in a much deeper correspondence between the processes of nature and the rhythm of the human tragedy. Here are some verses which he sent back to me that Easter, composed in the memory of the Barston cherry orchards:

The cherry-tree is white and fresh
With blossom for the day,
For every year at Easter-time
It blossoms, come what may.

And come what may, where blossom is,
There fruit will follow, too,
And cherries will be ripe and red
Before the summer's through.

He wrote it thinking that there would be a second front in 1943, in which, like many others, he was mistaken. His cynicism was not wholly cynicism. On the denial of Original Sin the Towers of Babel have been built and are being built, and in their collapse the world has been drenched in blood and will be drenched in blood again. And Martin, as he afterwards told me, found it in his heart to be grateful to the oily and unpleasant Levantine, who bore the marks of fallen nature so clearly stamped upon his features and saved him from the vision of the Rosy Dawn.

Martin was a good soldier for very much the same reasons as he was a good cricketer and was naturally well dressed. It was easy to him to perform physical feats and intolerable to him to perform them badly. He was, as he himself put it in one letter, 'a good soldier because he would have felt such a bloody fool being a bad one.' And he was a glad soldier because he was still young enough to feel delight at the discovery of courage. We all wonder how we shall acquit ourselves when first we come face to face with death. Life has few greater exhilarations than the discovery that we do not very much mind. It is often said that you can only expect men to fight well in war if you exclude from their mind all doubt about the utter rightness and necessity of their cause, about the complete depravity of the enemy. For the generality this may be true. But there are some who fight all the better if they are allowed to shut their minds to all questioning about the cause and to fight the war simply as if it were a game to be played. A friend wrote of Martin's uncle, who was killed in the last war:

> Because he was not clever, brave or rich,
> He went and died at St. Germain-de-Give,
> Fighting most nobly for a cause in which
> He did not in the very least believe.

Martin was something of the same timber. Perhaps to say that he fought the war as if it were a game is the wrong way to put it. Perhaps one should rather say that the best soldiers of all are those who rise above hatred, who rise above the immediate political aims of their country, which are always confused by complications, and who see it as the real aim of the war to show to the world that one can fight well and still fight as a gentleman. For these alone carry with them a hope not only of victory, but of a better world beyond victory, of the world without hate.

The only thing in the whole war, as far as I ever heard, that made him angry was the account of the feat by which he earned the Military Cross. It was a very good Military Cross and won him a certain volume of publicity. In the battle he had captured an Italian mortar. He knew nothing about Italian mortars and had very little aptitude for mechanics. But after, as he a little characteristically put it, 'fiddling about with it,' he somehow, and much to his surprise, got it to work, turned it, and put out of action an enemy machine-gun. This, gallant enough as it was, was all in the casual day's work. It was a detail that raised the controversy. At the height of the action a British tank that had been captured by the Germans drove up, and Martin gave it a cheery wave, 'mistaking it,' said the newspaper story, 'for one still manned by our men.' It was this phrase that sent Martin red.

'Of course I did not mistake it,' he said. 'I knew perfectly well that it was manned by the Germans. Why, it was firing at me all the time.'

'What did you wave at it for, then?' asked the other officers.

'Oh, just for fun,' said Martin.

'But the bloke was trying to kill you,' they said.

'Of course,' said Martin. 'Whatever has that got to do with it? Surely you wouldn't hate a man just because he was killing you. I've never heard worse reasoning in my life.'

'But what would you do then?' they asked.

'Kill him back, of course,' said Martin.

Then, when the fighting was on the Mareth Line, came through the news—a telegram to Ruth that Martin was missing. I was not with Ruth at the time, but George happened to be staying there, and no woman, I am sure, could have asked for a nobler, a more tender or a wiser counsellor. Even Ruth's great fortitude faltered for a bit. She, like the other Fossetts, had none of the easy comfort of a belief in our cause, in the superficially political sense. She had no shadow of belief that any such good as permanent peace or economic improvement would come out of the war. Nor did George seek to comfort her by correcting that deep scepticism. He had none of that sort of faith himself. He did not think that the world would be a comfortable place after the war, and he did not even think that it would be a very good thing if it were. But what he did think important—even as Bobby had thought it important—was that men should prove themselves at the test that is sent to them, that, if courage is required, they should show courage. The pattern of the world has become now so inextricably confused that none but the feeble-minded still prophesy what will be the consequence of any particular act of victory. Yet wisdom still knows that somehow good faith and virtue and courage will be found worth while in this world or the next and cling the more certainly to their knowledge through the very confusion of the times.

It was in this fundamental faith—the only faith that matters—that Ruth for a moment faltered on this day of the telegram.

'What evidence have you that it's all worth while, George?' she said. 'You say so; you say that Christ said so. But why should not all these comforts have been invented by fools to cheat themselves? Because they cannot face the reality that nothing matters, they make up all these tales about values and worth-while. But suppose it's all a story told by an idiot, and your values are the worst lie of all? Suppose that Ibsen's right and your God is an old man whom you cheat?'

And then at that very moment the telephone rang, and it was I (a little irregularly) to tell her of a tale that I had picked up at the War Office that there was some reason to think that Martin had been on a raiding party which had got lost and surrounded—that he might well be a prisoner and that it was by no means necessary to give up hope.

A few days afterwards his name was announced on the Vatican Radio and it was confirmed that he was in Italy, and some weeks after that cheerful letters began to dribble through from him at irregular intervals. He had no complaints save of the inadequacy of the food and the lack of female company. He liked his Italian guards and used to gossip with them in his moderate, if somewhat broken,

Italian about their families, and they would show him grinning pictures of their innumerable children, to whom they professed, with obvious sincerity, an undying devotion.

He of course was not allowed to write at the time of their political opinions, but afterwards, when he got back to England, he told us of the judgment that he had formed of them. Democracy, Liberalism, Fascism were, he found, to these men concepts wholly without meaning. They were neither for them nor against them. To their minds government, whatever the form of government, was 'they'—a distant gang, apart from themselves, who taxed them and ordered them about. So it had been in the past. So it was now. So, they had no doubt whatever, it would be in the future.

As for the war, they were firmly convinced that the relations between nations must inevitably be relations of master and servants. They had always been servants in the past, and they thought in their heart of hearts that there was little doubt that they would be servants again in the future. A tradition of centuries made them sceptical of any hope that an Italian enterprise would be carried through to success. Still, there was just a chance that Mussolini would get away with it—just a chance, not indeed that he would win, but that he had backed a winner, and then what fun! And then how they would cheer and laugh and chatter as they sat upon the throne of the world and saw Englishmen and Americans and, best of all, Frenchmen abase themselves before their feet!

'But what did they imagine that they would do to us when they had won?' I asked.

'Oh, they were entirely childish about that,' he said. 'It was all just a matter of Roman triumphs, and what a joke it would be to make the boss clean your boots! They always reminded me of Marlowe. You remember,

Is it not brave to be a king?
Is it not passing brave to be a king,
And ride in triumph, through Persepolis?

'And did they think that they would ride in triumph through Persepolis,' I asked, 'even if the Axis won? Did they think that the Germans would let them?'

'Oh, they had no illusions about the Germans,' he said, 'but they made this war a sort of test-case of Mussolini's astuteness. If he proved himself clever enough to bluff his way through this war, then they felt convinced that he would find some way of double-crossing the Germans and turning the tables on them after the war. They had no idea how he would do this. They were quite prepared to leave it to him, but in their heart of hearts they did not really believe that he could get away with this war—at least, not by the time that I got there. And with the Sicilian landing they knew that the game was up and the bluff was called. Then, of course, they became absolutely charming and pro-British and anti-Fascist, and were even prepared to say that they believed in democracy if one would give them an English cigarette. I had made a cricket ball of a sort of some rags sewn together in a piece of leather, and we had smoothed out a pitch, and, when we had not quite enough players, we made the Italian warders field for us.'

'Were they any good?' I asked.

'Oh no,' he said; 'they fetched the ball. One could not say much more than that. I do not remember any of them ever stopping anything, much less catching it.'

'Did they ever bat?' I asked.

'I made one man bat as a punishment,' said Martin, 'because he had tried to knife me. They would all have gladly knifed me, I expect, a few months earlier, when they expected Mussolini to ride into Cairo, but they thought it a mistake to do so when he was just about to be beaten. So they all agreed that I could make the would-be assassin go in to bat and bowl body-line at him, provided that I promised not to report the camp when Italy surrendered. It was rather fun.'

'I must say that I don't think that they sound so frightfully attractive,' I said.

'Oh, I don't know,' said Martin, 'I had given the poor fellow a good deal of provocation. I had told him that he reminded me of a constipated version of Great-Uncle Dotty, and described in a few brief sentences all that that implied. You know, Peter, I can't really hold it much against a person that he wants to kill me—not, I mean, those who are made that way. There are so many worse things that people do to one.'

'Such as?" I asked.

'Oh, literary blokes, asking one to praise what they have written, for instance,' he said. 'Like the people one used to meet at the Dawns' parties. That is much worse than murder.'

'The rights and wrongs of war are a curious business,' he added. 'One day they brought in two French officers as prisoners. The Italians told me that they questioned them about their opinions. One said that he would fight on against France's enemies until her soil was free. The other said that everything was now so complicated that it was no longer possible to tell what policy or whose victory would turn out for good or bad. I agreed with the second man, but thought that he was a swine to say so—I don't quite know why. And I did not think it in the least likely that France ever would be free again in the sense in which the first man hoped, but I thought his line was the only decent line to take when one was a prisoner. One can't criticise a cause when one's serving it.'

When the Italian armistice came we, of course, had hopes in the first confusion that the Allies would immedi-

6

ately succeed in seizing all Italy. Martin, as far as we could make out, had not been moved to Germany, unless in the very last days before the armistice. Therefore, as his camp seemed to have been somewhere in Central Italy, our hopes were high. Then came the German re-establishment of themselves in Rome and the centre, the vague stories about Allied prisoners drifting about the countryside or joining up with anti-Fascist Italians, German threats to them to return to prison, and all once more was anxiety.. We heard no news until six weeks later a telegram came, followed an hour or two after on the same day by Martin in person. His experiences had been very much the same as those of many other Allied prisoners. On proclamation of the armistice he had been let out of the camp and had planned to make his way down from the hills into Rome, which he expected to find in Allied occupation and where he thought that he would be able to report to an Allied officer. There were no regular trains running, and he had to travel as best he could by hops on infrequent lorries, carts or whatever there might be. It was not until he was within five miles of Rome that he learnt that the Germans were in occupation there. Then, turning on his tracks, he set out, as did so many others, to walk south to the British lines near Naples. There were others who made the long trek from camps in the far north of Italy—sometimes a trek of as long as four or five hundred miles. Martin, starting from near Rome, had less than a hundred miles to go. It cannot therefore be claimed that his was an exceptional adventure. Like others, he walked from farmhouse to farmhouse, missing the large towns and finding but little difficulty in avoiding the Germans, who, intent on building and manning their winter line, had small interest in scouring the Apennines for stray British prisoners. There was of course a reward offered for his delivery, but not one of the desperately poor Italian peasants, at whose houses Martin called for refuge, seemed even to dream of handing him over.

'It was not that they were particularly pro-British,' he told me. 'They weren't. Their one interest had been to keep the war off Italian soil, and they were rather annoyed with the British for being so slow in fixing things up with Badoglio that they failed to do this.'

'Why didn't they give you up, then?' I asked. 'Was it just that they were afraid that, if they did, they would get it in the neck when the Allies came?'

'Oh no,' he said, 'I don't think that they thought as far ahead as that. It was just that the poor don't give people up. The poor are at their best with prisoners. They have a great sense that it is a spin of the coin who is in jug and who is not, and that all poor people are schoolboys linked together against the master and that they must not sneak. You will find that in every country, and poor people who will do anything else in the wide world for money will yet draw the line at informing. I don't think that the Highlanders were all so awfully Jacobite in the '45. It was just that they would not give up Prince Charlie, simply because he was on the run. They would not have told on a poacher either.'

Prison, for all the idiosyncrasies of the guards, he found boring, but this fortnight of escaping across country, exhausting as it was, he on the whole enjoyed. 'Almost as good as war,' he said that it was, and told us how the Italians were amazed at his youth. He added—whether truly or not I cannot say; I dare say that it was true—that they exclaimed that he was like a Greek god.

'Hermes perhaps on top,' said Martin, 'but a pair of matchsticks underneath,' for the walking had worn down his legs into straight, narrow rods.

The anecdote of the whole adventure that pleased his humour most was at a cinema in Naples which he visited after he had reached English safety. An American war film was shown in order to arouse the enthusiasm of the Italian populace. At the climax of the film the hero, jilted by the heroine, exclaimed, 'Then I will go to Europe and fight for the cause of democracy.' A roar of laughter from every quarter of the cinema greeted what appeared to the audience to be the supreme comic come-back of the film.

All abstract arguments about the advantages of town-life or country, of the life of adventure or of the stay-at-home, are in a measure futile, for the wise life must be lived according to the motif of alternate immersion and retirement. One acquires abroad the breadth and wisdom that then enables one to live profitably at home. So Martin, glad to have been to the war and prepared to go back again as long as the war was on, had, he confessed, yet learnt at the war that adventure was not his true home. His true home was among his own people, and he must return at last to the Somerset land, and, like Eldred in the Ballad of the White Horse,

> Even as he strode like a pestilence
> That strides from Rhine to Rome,
> He thought how tall his beans might be,
> If ever he came home.

'One can't go on wandering for very long,' he told his mother. Although perhaps he was not even yet intellectually quite mature, after Italy spiritually he had jumped the 'space between.'

XIII

For all George's theological consolation, I was glad indeed that Ruth was spared the trial of the second loss. There is a limit to each person's strength, spiritual as well as physical, and the old Adam in me could not, I confess, altogether conceal a little sardonic amusement at noticing the confidence with which Ruth found the consolations of the Christian religion intellectually satisfying as soon as Martin's return had made certain that she did not for the moment personally need them.

'You're an old fraud,' I said one day to George; 'you're a fraud in just the same way as Johnson said that people who were always trying to persuade you that poverty was not an evil were frauds. When you think that Martin's dead, you tell Ruth to fall down on her knees and praise the Lord and say that this was the best thing that could possibly happen just because it is the Lord's will. But, when you find that Martin is alive after all, you're as pleased as Punch and tell Ruth how glad you are and go about saying that it's good news—almost as if you were a human being.'

I had not meant the silly gibe very seriously, but I was, I must confess, a little surprised when George, for the first time in all my knowledge of him, seemed to be a trifle nettled.

'Look here, Peter,' he said, quite harshly, 'are you running this universe or is Almighty God?'

I am not sure that I quite followed the point of his question, but I acknowledged that my gibe had been a foolish one and did not pursue it.

High Churchmen and Roman Catholics, by insisting on their celibacy, wish, I suppose, to make their priests impersonal instruments of Divine consolation. The reality, indeed, about the difference between the Catholic and the Protestant is just the opposite of what is commonly said. To the Catholic God speaks, and it is a matter of very secondary importance what is the name of the particular priest through whose mouth He speaks. But it is the Protestant who, rightly or wrongly, allows another individual to come between the individual and his Maker. For among

Protestants the parson speaks, consoles, advises, admonishes as a person. There is no attempt to depersonalise him, to shut him behind a grille, to pretend that he only speaks as an instrument of the Church. I do not pretend to say which is the better plan. I must confess that neither of priests nor of parsons has my experience been sufficient to justify me in an opinion. But George pressed his consolations upon Ruth with such a vigour that I almost thought for a time that it was his hope to make himself my brother-in-law. Ruth even once or twice feared as much too, and confided her fears to me. We both agreed that in principle we approved of Dr. Johnson's opinion that a second marriage was a great compliment to the first spouse, but we agreed also that one married in practice and not on principle and that neither of us had as yet met anyone who at all tempted us to a second venture. 'I do hope that George won't ask me,' Ruth said. 'He's a dear, good creature, but I would sooner marry a wet policeman.'

It turned out that we had miscalculated. George's spiritual consolations were not indeed disinterested, but it was not towards Ruth that his interest was directed. Marigold Arbuthnot, Tony's first cousin, had lost a brother in the last fighting in Africa, and it turned out that in doing so she had found a husband. I was delighted, though I must confess also a little surprised. Marigold was a nice, kind creature—a pleasant blue-eyed, all too Nordic blonde, with many more morals and much less humour than her cousin. I should have called her what the newspapers describe as 'the average voter'—indeed, were it not that she was almost six feet tall and of the female sex, she was almost 'the little man 'of the newspapers himself. I should have expected her to be of the type which demanded to be shown that our cause was a cause of right and democracy, whose victory would bring with it security and perpetual peace. George's political scepticism and metaphysical consolations would, I thought, alike have left her cold. But the outcome gave a certain confirmation to George's contention that the deeper arguments were missed by the average person, not because they were inordinately difficult but only because they were unfamiliar. One often finds that those who by some accident are lucky enough to be illiterate think naturally on the spiritual plane. It is only the constant reiteration of the daily newspaper which drives the others to follow after the will-o'-the-wisp that problems are capable of a purely political solution. Those few who have so much as heard that there be a Holy Ghost generally believe in Him.

There was, in spite of, perhaps because of, her simplicity, a reserve of strength and understanding in Marigold. She always somehow reminded me of that strange, powerful line of Dante—'ladies who have intelligence of love'—a line which does not mean as you, gentle reader, perhaps imagine, 'ladies who have had sexual experience,' but 'ladies who have a metaphysical notion what love is about'—a rarer accomplishment. So far from being repelled by George's political scepticism, so far from finding in that scepticism a confirmation that her brother's death had been in vain, she, on the contrary, found in his teaching a satisfactory consolation. Who was I to be surprised, since I myself had both needed and learnt exactly the same lesson? And when George told us that the upshot of it all—or at least one upshot of it all—was that Marigold had consented to be his wife, we were delighted, for she was a girl who had the roots of virtue in her and at the same time enough Arbuthnot blood for virtue not to be too angular or too oppressive, and Ruth, like the lady in Bernard Shaw's play, exclaimed, 'How splendid! how glorious! . . . but, oh, what an escape!'

The escape was in one quarter at any rate, it seems, unexpected. Robert had always cultivated a detached interest in weddings. At the age of six he was once heard to remark as he emerged from the church, 'Daddy, I should like to come with you to the conception. Please, Daddy, can't I come with you to the conception?' Now, Ruth's handwriting was not notably legible, and she always used to refer to Marigold as M. She wrote to Robert the news, saying, with some casualness in the midst of other news, 'Uncle George is going to marry M.' Robert misread the 'M' as 'me,' but received the news in a spirit as casual as that in which it was given. 'Dear Mummy,' he wrote back, 'Congrats on getting engaged to Uncle George. I made fifty-one not out in Juniors yesterday. Good-bye from Robert.' Ruth wrote to correct him, and Robert accepted the correction by beginning the next letter, 'Dear Mummy, I am so glad to hear that you are not going to marry Uncle George.'

At least I was most delighted for George's sake that he was going to achieve the condition of matrimony. Intensely and properly proud of his priesthood, he yet had a curious social humility about being a clergyman. He was never what P. G. Wodehouse might have called 'a clergyman's clergyman'—that is to say, he never moved very largely in clerical circles—principally because he so very rarely came across clergymen who were interested in religion. His companions were of the laity, but he was very sensitive to the feeling that among the laity many thought of a clergyman as an absurd being and disliked his presence. Being scrupulously fair-minded, he was unwilling to dismiss this harsh judgment as only a prejudice. He tried hard with all openness of mind to see the point of view, but then, he plaintively confessed, 'with all the will in the world to be fair, when I listen to the opinions of those people who call clergymen absurd, I find their opinions to be so often of such a degree of silliness that I can hardly believe that any man born of woman can be found to utter them. I do not know where to look in my embarrassment at such silliness. What ought I to do about it?'

Marigold was a section officer in the W.A.A.F.s—freckly, red hair, full lips. One could not call her beautiful, but she was pleasant-looking and full of laughter, a gelotophil.

'You are very beautiful, Marigold,' George said to her—or so she told me.

'Am I the most beautiful thing in all the world?' asked Marigold, who was quite without illusions and knew very well that she was nothing of the sort.

'Of course you aren't,' said George snortily, with his passion for accurate statement. 'No woman is half as beautiful as a horse or a daffodil. Nevertheless, you are very beautiful.'

She had the great virtue of constant high spirits which, as a virtue, is so much underrated. How great a comfort it is in a person that we should be able to feel confident that he will be always cheerful and in good temper! How strangely people neglect their duty to keep themselves so! As she was at a distant station, I did not often run into her these days, but it chanced that I met her in Oxford Street the day after the announcement of the engagement.

'Hullo, stranger,' I said.

'Hullo, Peter,' she answered. 'What are you doing here?'

'At the moment offering my congratulations to the bride of the season,' I said.

'And thank you for that,' she said.

'Come and have some tea.'

We pushed our way into a neighbouring café and with some difficulty procured some attention.

'Sugar?' I asked.

'Certainly not,' she said. 'That is the new threat that the war has brought us. Sugar's so short these days that in canteens and N.A.A.F.I.s it is almost impossible to get tea without it. It's my real treat to get somewhere where I can get unsweetened tea.'

'Well, are you glad that you're going to be married?' I asked.

'Of course I am,' she answered. 'Otherwise I should not be going to be married.'

'Oh, I don't know,' I said. 'People do all sorts of things against their better judgments.'

'Oh, I hate people not being married,' she said. 'Why don't you get married, Peter?'

'I've nothing against it in theory, my dear,' I said, 'but after all one can't quite pick up a wife by just going out into the street and whistling for her as if she were a cab.'

'I can't see why not,' said Marigold. 'That seems to be about what most people do these days.'

'Yes, but it doesn't appear to work out very satisfactorily,' I said.

'Well, take Tony,' she said. 'He's always being married.'

'Yes, but I can't imagine why,' I said. 'After all, if you don't believe in marriage, why do you get married? It puts a lot of unnecessary money into the lawyers' pockets getting out of it again.'

'Yes,' she said, 'so tiresome. Whenever he asks me to lunch he has to put me off because he's got to go and get divorced. It's such a bore, because he is really quite amusing. Thank God I'm marrying a clergyman. I can't imagine how girls come to marry laymen these days.'

Marigold, even in more serious mood, did not feel the least this abhorrence of the cloth which George so much feared.

'It's so interesting,' she said. 'He tells me all about the mysteries of the faith—what the resurrection of the body really means and how clergymen's collars fasten up behind, which I had always longed to know. Do you know that they don't have a front stud at all? Their shirts are just open at the front behind—well—behind all that.'

I replied that George was a liberal-minded man and a rationalist, but that I had no doubt that there were clergymen to whom such openness would seem dangerously latitudinarian.

'Oh,' she said, 'do you think that there are schools of shirt, too?"

'Tell me, Marigold,' I said, 'if it's not a rude answer—I am very anxious to know—will you mind having children?'

'It's like oysters,' she said. 'You can't tell whether you will like them till you've tried them. I haven't any especially strong maternal yearnings at the prospect, but that's neither here nor there. It's a matter of supply and demand. People like me usually go dotty about the brats when they appear.'

'It'll put a bit of a stopper on your peripatetic habits,' I said. For she was one of those girls whose way it had been never to stay in the same place for more than two days on end.

'No marriages work less well,' she said, 'than those in which the parties think that they don't have to change any of their pre-marriage habits.'

'I agree,' I said. 'Nothing in the world is quite so boring as never doing anything that is in the least boring. Life's only tolerable through contrasts.'

I at once rang up George and asked him to lunch, and we toasted his happiness in Algerian wine at an excellent little Dickensian inn near Victoria, whose name I do not reveal for fear that others might rob me of my privacy there.

'To tell the truth, George,' I said, 'I always used to think that you were one of those fellows who believed in the celibacy of the clergy.'

'Why should you think that?' he asked. 'England has

been made by parsons' sons. The possession of them is the great advantage that we have over Catholic countries.'

'Oh, I always thought that the sort of parsons who talked about the Resurrection were celibates, and the sort that talked about the Beveridge Report had children,' I said. 'You belong to the first sort.'

'The analysis does not seem to be entirely exhaustive,' said George, smiling, as he sipped his wine.

There were moods in which George refused to be serious and to satisfy my comparatively fitful and flickering interest in matters religious. This, the day of his engagement, was, perhaps justifiably, such a day. Naturally, his indifference stimulated my enthusiasm.

'The Church of England seems to me the most extraordinary institution on the face of the earth,' I said.

'Doubtless,' said George, with a languid sip. 'For any particular reason?'

'I can't think why it doesn't catch on more,' I said. 'It seems to me that it ought exactly to suit modern needs. It cuts out hell and all that.'

'It does nothing of the sort,' put in George.

'Oh, I know that you believe in hell,' I said, 'but that's just a fad of your own. At least in the C. of E. you're allowed to believe that God's something approaching a gentleman.'

'Man made God in his own image,' said George sarcastically.

'Perhaps,' I said. 'You can make fun of it if you want. But is it not exactly what everybody believes? The one real difficulty about the Church of England always used to be that, whatever they might say about branches of the Catholic Church and so on, it did seem to make out the English to be a chosen people. Up to 1940 this seemed the most ridiculous of all dogmas, and then suddenly in one blazing, finest hour it became the most plausible.'

'My God, George,' I went on, 'if I were doing the rhetoric for your Church, I would make things hum. I would have great purple passages about God moving in a mysterious way, about unworthy instruments little understanding what they did, the truth in its pure form surviving only in one little island, no one could guess why, and then in time that island sending out its children to colonise all the quarters of the earth. And so on and so on up till 1940. Freedom dead in all the world and surviving only because of the guts of the people of this one little island. So at last everyone could see God gave His special revelation to the people of England—you know, like Milton, "and especially to His Englishmen." I can't think why you don't put it across more. I mean to say, just look at foreigners. Honestly, George, you've got all the cards in your hands. All you need is publicity.'

'*Porro unum necessarium*,' said George. 'Thanks frightfully, Peter. What a delightful prospect! What would you have us do about it? Ordain Lord Beaverbrook? Won't you have this drink with me?'

But I was interested in the line of reflection on which my mind had struck. It was as new to me as to my hearer and, like Bishop Blougram, I believed, say, half I said. Yet it did strike me that there was something in it.

'Well, this is what always seems to me so odd about the Church of England,' I said. 'It's in a sort of conspiracy to pretend that it's dead. You parsons are always complaining about having no influence and your churches being empty. And for years, as you went there and I didn't, I assumed that what you said was true. But now as I go about the world—at the club, for instance, at the War Office—I am continually coming across perfectly ordinary tough, practical he-men, and it slips out in some little accident of their conversation that they slunk off to church last Sunday.'

However, there was no drawing George that day.

'My dear Peter,' he said, 'I am indeed delighted to hear of the edifying spiritual company that you keep, but I am really not going to preach you a sermon after two glasses of excellent port.'

'I never asked you to,' I said. 'I asked you to stop me preaching you one.'

'That is indeed a more desperately urgent problem,' said George. 'I think that I had better go to the lavatory. It seems the only really safe solution.'

XIV

WE sallied out into the street. I wanted to walk back to the War Office, and George, too, was anxious for a breath of air, stipulating only for his destination that it should not be the Ministry of Information. A strange sight met our eyes when we reached Whitehall. The opposite pavement was occupied by a long string of young men and women, all of military age. At first I thought that it was just a crowd, but on a second inspection I saw that it was a procession. A less attractive procession I have never met. With vacuous faces, with slouching gait, hands in pockets, overcoats half on and half off, this curious company edged along the pavement. It recited to itself in a dull, low, dreary, monotonous whine, 'Lock the Fascists up, lock the Fascists up.' It was the day after the Mosley release. The Jacquerie had come to town. The people of England was on its lower middle-class way to protest at the Home Office.

'Lot o' folk don't seem to have a job o' work to do,' said a navvy by my side.

'Course they haven't. They're the lot that's on strike at the chemical works,' said his mate.

I have no idea whether this was true or not. They did not look to me as if they belonged to the working class at all or as if they ever had a job from which to strike, and why they were not in the Army I cannot imagine. But at least this gibe about their strike was the common gibe of the streets.

To me, as to so many people, the agitation on the Mosley release was the final deathblow to my left-wing opinions, in any technical sense of that phrase. I hope that I preserve my charity, as I certainly preserve my admiration, for the British working man. But charity and admiration for the working man have little connection with left-wing politics. I am a man for the rule of law, a *habeas corpus* man. I agree with Dr. Johnson that *habeas corpus* is the one great advantage which Englishmen have over foreigners. As small a time ago as when I was at school, before the war of 1914, I used to read about the *lettres de cachet* of pre-Revolutionary France and wonder at the wickedness and tyranny under which they could exist. Never did I dream that I could live to see such things in England and to see a serious threat that they would become a permanent part of our life. Neither I nor, so far as I am aware, any other defender of Mosley's release took our stand through any wish to apologise for Mosley's opinions. Mosley's merits or demerits were an irrelevance. The rule of law says that a man shall not be deprived of his freedom because his opinions are unpopular. He shall be deprived of it only if he be proved after fair trial to be guilty of a crime. If the rule of law goes, all freedom goes.

Naturally I well understood that these were not the people who would be our masters if ever the Left should come to power, and that it was not fair to judge the mentality of the Left by their mentality. The philosophy of the Left, as of the Nazis, is a perfectly logical philosophy, granted its premises. They are both, in the most proper sense of a much abused word, idealists. It is the assertion of both of these philosophies that

> it is more blessed for the rippling pool
> To be engulfed in the great ocean stream.

Their faith is the faith of Shigalev in Dostoievsky's *Possessed*, the faith which holds that the individual must be sacrificed entirely to society and to the power which arrogates to itself the right to speak in the name of society. 'All are slaves and equal in their slavery' is Shigalev's equalitarian creed. Ordinary men, explains Shigalev's friend, 'must entirely renounce all personality and become, so to speak, a herd in order through absolute obedience by a series of regenerations to regain their natural innocence.' 'They will all be happy,' says the Inquisitor in *The Brothers Karamazov*, 'all the millions, except the hundred thousand who rule over them. For we alone, we who guard the mystery, we alone shall be unhappy. There will be thousands of millions of happy children, and only a hundred thousand martyrs, who have taken on themselves the curse of the knowledge of good and evil.'

Both in Russia and in Germany this faith has proved itself capable of inspiring so intense a devotion that it is idle to speak of it only as a madness or to condemn its masters as mere gangsters. It is clear that it satisfies some very deep need of human nature which the secularist Liberalism which it supplanted failed to satisfy. It even, it appears, can inspire men willingly to denounce and accuse themselves to death, when they are convinced that by doing so they can serve the cause. We cannot condemn the Left's cynicism in using the Jacquerie until we have first shown that the claims of justice and freedom and individual rights are valid.

Michael argued once, when I debated this with him, that Christianity did not invent asceticism; it controlled it.

What he called 'unaided man' had always oscillated, as we see from Oriental history, between extravagances of indulgence and extravagances of asceticism, between debauchery and self-mutilation, like that of the priests of Attis. The Christian Church imposed a balanced discipline and repressed the extravagances in either direction. In the same way 'unaided man' oscillated between anarchy and tyranny. In the Greco-Roman-Christian world alone did you find any attempt to strike between these extremes the mean of ordered freedom.

'The claims of your Church,' I said, 'are just as totalitarian as those of the Bolsheviks or the Nazis.'

'But no,' he said, 'because in the Christian society the authority itself, the Church, insists upon the necessity for freedom and justice. Hitler or Stalin can make up what they like and call it law. But the Pope cannot make up anything. He is bound by the Church's own teaching and nature and history. He is tied to the defence of his own dogma that God cares for justice and for every individual soul.'

'That may be all very well in theory,' I said, 'but what has the practice been in such a country as—shall we say?—Spain? How much liberty does the Church in fact allow there?'

'I don't know very much about Spain,' said Michael, 'but certainly I do not deny that Christians have often failed in practice to strike the right balance between liberty and authority. But it's like Dr. Johnson and a dog standing on its hind legs. It's not that Christians have always solved the problem rightly, but that no other sort of society has even tried to solve it at all.'

'The Greeks?' I said.

'Oh, I count them in,' he answered. 'Greek thought was all leading up to Christianity and asking the questions to which Christianity gave the answer. If justice is just a bourgeois prejudice, then there is no particular reason why politicians should not use the Jacquerie for their own purposes and why one should not put innocent people to death if they are inconvenient.'

'It's much what God does,' I said; 'always striking people down in an apparently arbitrary way and then telling us to believe that it is all for the best, though we can't expect to understand how.'

'Exactly,' he said, 'but then God, as Queen Elizabeth so truly remarked, is "without body, parts or passions." What is so horrible about the totalitarian policy is that it is carried out, nominally, on behalf of an unreal abstraction, really on behalf of some individuals who are, at the very least, as imperfect as the rest of us. I don't deny that there is something a bit impressive about the German or Russian pictures of the future—the abolition of petty frontiers and class divisions, and mean personal ambitions all subordinated to the general good of the brave new world; and when they tell us that this new unity, which the new technique demands, can only be achieved through some preliminary war and ruthlessness and cruelty and tyranny; that there must be a period of the dictatorship of the proletariat or a period of the domination of the master-race, well, it all sounds quite plausible. In a certain mood, indeed, the ruthlessness even seems to give a kind of rugged grandeur to the dream. But, if there be one lesson of history, it is that man cannot foresee the future. History is littered with these visions of what is to come, no single one of which has ever been proved true. The unexpected always turns up. That being so, our tradition is quite right in refusing to allow people to do evil that good may come, if only because no one knows whether it will come or not. Planning is all very well so long as we pay the homage to our own lack of prevision by keeping our plans subject to the demands of justice. It has always seemed to me that justice is in the judgment of régimes the test virtue. A régime which knowingly punishes a man for a crime which he has not committed is a wicked régime.'

I quite agree with Michael about the importance of justice, but I doubt if it is so exclusively ecclesiastical a virtue as he seemed to imply. Justice has had a not ignoble history in England, and the machinery of the State, just as much as of the Church, has often been used to defend liberty rather than to oppress it. But, again, perhaps George is right when he says that this was indeed true when the State was administered by Christian men, but that it is most uncertain how far it will be true when the State is no longer so administered.

That night I dined with Uncle Dotty. Michael Paravane was there too. Michael collected 'awful old men' with a kind of ghoulish delight, as if he were a character in Edgar Allan Poe—M. Waldemar, for instance—collecting deliquescence. There is nothing in this world more beautiful than the serene, dignified, tranquil old age of acceptance. But such was not Uncle Dotty's old age. He was an old man in the worst possible sense of the word, endowed with a rare genius for folly.

He used to like to have Michael Paravane about because Michael was a Papist. Uncle Dotty was a blaspheming old non-believer, and such men in their old age often like to keep company with a Catholic, with whom they imagine that they can spar. Twenty years ago, in a memorable moment, Uncle Dotty had said, 'Never was there a time when people were more decent to each other, and never was there a time when priests had less power.' A lot of people had then agreed with him—twenty years ago—and so Uncle Dotty, poor man, had gone on saying it ever since, not noticing.

With a violence that only equalled his inconsistency he combined offensively blatant expressions of patriotism with a selfish grousing at any inconveniences that he might suffer. He denounced black marketers, but he denounced with yet more vigour the servants if they were not able in the fourth year of war to provide him with every comfort which he enjoyed in peace. As the shadows of war lengthened out from year to year, Uncle Dotty's conversation continued as boring and his table as groaning as ever they had been before Neville Chamberlain flew to Berchtesgaden.

'How does he manage to keep it up?' I asked a little wonderingly.

'There's something rather splendid in being as awful as all that, isn't there?' said Michael.

'You've got a very comfortable place here, Uncle Dotty,' I said to him once, looking round his very easy drawing-room.

'And so I ought to have,' he said, 'seeing that I've spent all my life looking after Number One.'

We dined that night in the grill-room of the Huntingdon, where Uncle Dotty had been for years a well-known and unpopular figure, and where he had a *bête noire* of a waiter—a poor, harmless little man called Wilkins, whom Uncle Dotty erroneously imagined to be called Jenkins.

'You damned Papists,' he said to Michael, 'I would never allow any priest to tell me what I should read.'

Michael exploded like an elephant into his soup. The notion of Uncle Dotty, whose reading was confined to the Jane strip in the *Daily Mirror*, ploughing through Gibbon's *Decline and Fall of the Roman Empire* just because the Pope told him not to, struck Michael as irresistibly comic.

'Bomb Rome, bomb Florence,' boomed Uncle Dotty into the night. 'All those damned pictures or whatever it is that they have there—what does it matter if they are hit? They only put ideas into people's heads.'

'If we back these damned Fascists in Lithuania we shall never hold the seat in West Worcester,' he said.

'The people in Lithuania aren't Fascists,' said Michael.

'The people in West Worcester think they are,' said Uncle Dotty. 'That's all that matters when there's an election in West Worcester.'

I tried him out on the Mosley case.

'Lock 'em all up,' was Uncle Dotty's first reaction. 'Fellow's a damned traitor—ought to be shot. Jenkins, some more claret.'

'But what should he be shot for?' asked Michael.

'I've told you,' said Uncle Dotty. 'For being a damned traitor, of course. Put him on trial and shoot him.'

'They've nothing to put him on trial for, that's just the point,' I argued.

I was even able to get Uncle Dotty's attention and to explain to him the difficulty that Mosley did not appear to be guilty of any crime, that if people were to be called criminals and shot just because one disagreed with them there would be an end of all freedom and all justice. I found Uncle Dotty a surprisingly easy convert, for in truth his only concern was to have violent opinions, and he cared very little what those opinions were.

'Oh, it's the other fellows are wrong, is it?' he said. 'A lot of Bolsheviks, are they? All right. Shoot the other fellows then. I don't care. That fellow Pritt—damned bad Wykhamist. Jenkins, some more claret.'

'No, Uncle Dotty,' I pleaded. 'I don't want the other fellows shot. The last thing that we want is the country running with blood and the people on top killing off the beaten party. Our whole tradition is that we have been able to live and let live under the law and tolerate a whole variety of opinions. It is that tradition that is in danger.'

But this was too much for Uncle Dotty, and his voice

trailed off into his coffee in protest against 'this damned highfaluting talk about not shooting people.'

Uncle Dotty was a monster but a symbol. He always went home immediately after dinner and then slept in his chair and snored from about a quarter to ten until half-past ten, when he woke with a start to exclaim, 'Has the all-clear gone yet?' and to help himself to whiskey. This evening Michael and I, being bored and revolted, agreed together to leave before the snoring. Uncle Dotty, who, like Sir Willoughby Patterne, entertained not that he might give pleasure to his guests but that he might save himself from the menace of solitude, protested. He tried to bribe us by advancing the time of whiskey by three-quarters of an hour. But we were adamant. So he called for 'six bills.' He was on the boards of six companies, so always had six bills so that he might charge them up on the different expense accounts. He paid the bill and offered us the change. It was his only form of generosity—and that a highly offensive one—to attempt to stand his guests the change after he had given them hospitality. Michael and I went together to the club and had our whiskey there.

'Generosity,' I said to Michael. 'That's the great need. That's what you must stand for if you go to Parliament.'

'It sounds sufficiently vague,' he said, 'even for a political programme, and would go very well—verbally at least—with Liberalism. Does it mean anything particular or is it just one of those things?'

'No,' I said, 'I mean just the opposite of everything that Uncle Dotty is. The great trick nowadays is to be for ever dividing society up into sheep and goats and pretending that the sheep are all right and that everything would be Utopia if only you got rid of the goats. You get it internationally, where just at the moment Germany happens to be the scapegoat nation, though I dare say that it will be somebody else ten years from now after the next war. You get it politically with all this hullabaloo about Munichers. You get it socially with the class-war talk. You get it in the loss of all distinction between disliking a man and calling him a criminal, which one finds in all these anti-Fascist and war-criminal-trial agitations.'

'Oh, I don't know that I'm in favour of letting the Germans down too lightly, if that's what you mean by generosity,' said Michael.

'Oh no, that's quite a different question,' I said. 'I am not discussing that at the moment. Do what you like to the Germans in the way of disarming them. If you really wish as a special act of war to shoot some of their leaders, since no one can think of anything else to do with them, then shoot them if you insist, though I do not see that it would do much good. But in any event do not call this justice, and do not say that there was a fair trial when there was not a fair trial, and do not call a man a criminal until he has been convicted of a crime. Truth is what really is at stake in all this, and truth is more important than any political programme. "Truth is the highest thing a man can keep." '

'Blood will have blood,' said Michael a little grimly. 'Macbeth was right.'

'Yes, but when is it going to stop?' I asked. 'You can't call trying war criminals justice unless you try ours as well as theirs. Perhaps they have a hundred times as many as we. Yet from what Martin told me about the fall of Tobruk we should have our little quota too.'

'Yes, but generosity's all very well,' said Michael, 'but there's something in *que messieurs les assassins commencent*. Some pretty vile things have been done in Europe in the last years—things that it almost makes one sick even to hear about.'

'Of course,' I said, 'but that's pathology, not crime. What

good would it do to repay all those poor brutes in their own coin?'

'I agree,' said Michael. 'The truth is that man by himself is pretty weak and animal and he needs authority to keep him on the rails at all. When authority itself becomes bestial, it's only to be expected that the instruments will become bestial too.'

'So the problem is to see to it that authority never again becomes bestial,' I said.

'Yes,' he agreed, 'you remember the Inquisitor in *The Brothers Karamazov*. When Christ met him He just kissed him.'

'Why did He do that?' I asked.

'It's very difficult to see what else He could have done.'

I was not absolutely certain what Michael meant by this. I was often not quite certain what he meant by his remarks.

He called a waiter and ordered some more drinks.

'I don't really believe,' I put in as my parting shot, 'that much good will come out of punishing even the individuals who have committed atrocities, but I am not for the moment arguing that the law should be reformed; I am arguing that it should not be violated. Punish those who have committed crimes against recognised codes, if you like, but that is a different issue.'

'I agree with all that. Bobby Fossett's Labour pal, Johnstone, made a rasping good speech to the Trades Union Congress the other day,' said Michael, 'Did you see it?'

'No,' I said.

'First, he denounced the lie-in-the-soul of those who pretended that the German people were not for the war. They did so, he said, not on any judgment of the facts, not because they knew or cared anything about the German people, but because it was a domestic political convenience to pretend that peoples never support aggressive wars. Then he turned and rent the Vansittartites, who spoke of punishment when they meant vengeance.'

'What we want,' I said, 'are guarantees against repetition, not external inquisition into the past. So here at home. If we take the record of all the parties before the war, they were all pretty wretched, and all plead, with a reasonable degree of plausibility, that they could not have done any better because the public would never have voted for them if they had proposed any more vigorous policy. The Fulham bye-election! Then the public say that they would have been more sensible if they had not been misled by the Press, and the Press says that it had to print what pleased people to keep the advertisers. Probably the truth is—which everybody knows and nobody dare say—that a foreign policy controlled by a democracy must inevitably be feeble and null and lead to war. The man-in-the-street never sees foreigners. How can he be expected to vote sensibly about them? Well, it's madness out of this mess to try to find an individual scapegoat. The only sensible maxim is Hamlet's, "to treat each man according to his deserts, and who shall 'scape whipping?"'

'I quite agree with you,' said Michael, 'about not having inquisitions into the past. But if democracy is inevitably incompetent in foreign policy, what hope is there of being more sensible in the future?'

'Obviously the only hope is to take foreign policy out of party politics,' I said. 'I do not mean, take it out by a law, but create a mental atmosphere where people who don't know anything about a subject refrain from screaming about it. It has done the Left no good—all this screaming even on the narrowest short-term calculation. It has not got them into power. Electorally the Right has probably gained more out of it than the Left. But the danger of it is that, while it has kept the Right in power, it has made it quite impossible for them to do anything sensible when they were there.'

'That's all very well,' said Michael, 'but you must remember that I am a Liberal and do believe in democracy. Besides, I don't know that I should be very likely to get in even down in Somerset on a programme of disfranchising all the electors.'

'Oh, I'm not against democracy,' I said. 'I don't really believe all that stuff that Bobby Fossett used to talk about government by gentlemen. There's something in it, of course, as there's something in most things. But it does not really make sense in the last analysis. I think that the people are admirable judges what sort of houses they want to have, what sort of food they want to eat, what sort of lives, indeed, they want to lead in general. I would far sooner have the decisions made by them than by Central Offices or by peripatetic Dons or Whitehall bureaucrats. I really do believe in fraternity as a literal fact. I really believe that men are brothers, that they have a common origin, that their differences of class or creed or nation, important as they may be, are yet enormously less important than what they have in common, and that you can appeal to them through their common humanity. But who else believes that? Does Uncle Dotty believe it?'

'Such a faith does not exactly shine out from his conversation,' agreed Michael.

'Did those fellows who went to-day to demonstrate in Whitehall against a dying man being let out of a prison to which he had never been condemned—after a number of eminent doctors had declared that his life was in danger and after a political opponent had decided that he was no longer able to be a public danger? Did they believe it?'

'Precisely not,' agreed Michael. 'A Fascist has become a sort of symbolic animal to them. They don't picture him as a creature of flesh and blood with a wife and children.'

'And, of course, the Fascists are, in their turn, exactly the same about Jews.'

'And I am coming across a new class of people,' said Michael, 'who say that they agree with the Fascists about the Jews, and with everybody else about the Fascists. 'Kill all Germans, Jews and Japs' is now the motto that is going the rounds of London's lavatories.'

'Our descendants will look back on our ideological wars as the last word in lunacy,' I said. 'Never was there more hatred, intolerance and general bloodiness—and at the end of it no one can give a coherent account of the differences between the ideologies that are tearing the world to pieces! Talk about Gibbon and Christendom fighting for an iota.'

'Yes,' agreed Michael, 'I object to calling Russia a democracy just because the Germans have attacked it. I will call the Russians brave, because they are. I will say that I hope that they will beat the Germans, because so I do. But I will not admit that we ought to grovel before them for the crime of having distrusted them before the war or that it was all our fault that they signed the Nazi-Soviet Pact.'

'All right,' I said. 'You're in on this, Michael. Let's form a Society to Prevent Ranting Against More Than Two or Three People. I will be treasurer and you will be secretary.'

'Right,' said Michael. 'But what happens when we have formed it?'

'Well, if I'm treasurer, you give me your subscription, of course.'

So, as was natural, the immediate problem was solved by our having two more drinks each, and then we dispersed to bed. I lay there meditating a little on what would come and what should come of all this. Naturally, I was not serious in my project of a Society to Prevent Ranting. There was far too much truth in the jest of the counter-title, which Michael produced over our drinks, that the

Society should rather be called Society for People Who Are Better Than Their Neighbours.

'Yes, Michael, and consist just of me and you,' I said, and with that sentence any project of organisation obviously died. I was never at the best of times much of a joiner, and a society for the promotion of fraternity would obviously go the way of all such societies of the last hundred and sixty years. It would degenerate into abuse and vilification of its neighbours who did not accept it, on the formula of '*Sois mon frère ou je te tue.*' Charity is something to be practised, not something to be advertised!

But that did not mean that I was not intensely sincere when I said that a tone of greater generosity in all our controversies, social, political, religious, was most sadly needed, and I did think equally sincerely that Michael Paravane was the sort of young man who might play his part in introducing that tone of generosity. He was one of those young men who, like Martin, had brought back from battle the clear distinction between fighting a man and hating him, and by the drawing of that distinction alone can we steer between the Scylla of hateful hatred and the Charybdis of intellectual collapse. I had always liked him, and over the last year had come to form a greater respect for his intellect than at first acquaintance. There was, I found, a good deal more in him than his somewhat absurd party politics, even though what it was I was not yet quite prepared to say. For there was a certain final elusiveness in his mind.

I found no reason in his intelligence to prophesy success for him in English political life. We have now reached a pass in that life where to be foolish is definitely an asset for the achievement of success. Folly in high place is, I think, no longer an accident, but, with the greatly increased pre-eminence of the Prime Minister, all positions short of leadership are now very deliberately filled with persons of quite inferior ability. All the last half-dozen Prime Ministers, whatever their other differences, have been alike with Atticus in their determination to 'bear like the Turk no brother near the throne.' Ability is a great handicap to success, and, combined with any further handicap, such as that of a good character, it is a quite fatal disqualification. As Michael was also handicapped by his religion, the chances of his attainment of any high office were very small.

Nevertheless, that was not wholly an evil. He was intelligent enough quickly to see how the land lay and not to waste his life in the futility of bitterness. The hopelessness of ambition might itself strengthen him in his disinterestedness. He had money, which, if money itself survived, would make it possible for him to continue in public life without reward, and his might well be a life of fruitful and important criticism.

Our only difficulty about him, as we got to know him better, was the difficulty of what he was really thinking on fundamentals. This was no obstacle when he was but an acquaintance, for one respects a man who, like William Watson,

> will not pay the world
> The evil and insolent courtesy
> Of offering it my baseness as a gift.

Nothing is more embarrassing and more insulting than too easy confidences—the chance train acquaintance who confesses to adultery or the strap-hanger in the Tube who airs his doubts about the Virgin Birth. But yet there comes a point where one feels that an inner door should be opened, and it is tantalising when that door is not opened.

In England, at any rate, this frustration is particularly common with Roman Catholic friends. Maybe the fault is partly—perhaps wholly—with us, Protestants or non-Catholics or whatever it is that we should be called. Perhaps we have been so free with our accusations that Catholics are for ever plotting to pervert us that they are naturally shy of talking to us about their fundamental beliefs. Anyway, they do not often talk of them in mixed company, and we Protestants, if we pride ourselves on being well bred, are equally careful not to say anything that may offend them. The result is to make conversation much more boring than it need be.

This came out a little amusingly when we were all down at Ruth's at Christmas-time. Michael had been over to see Margaret and—I suppose, incidentally, since it was unavoidable—to see the rest of us, and while he had been present the conversation had been friendly and light-hearted as one could wish, but assiduously general—the prospects of the war, the nature of the Turks, the nature of the Russians, the world that we were to look for after the war—the sort of conversation that must have taken place in almost every drawing-room in England that Christmas. Under the impulse of these stimuli a rare bottle of sherry vanished most pleasantly.

Then Michael had to get back to dinner, and there ensued that comedy which Catholicism so often causes in English social life. The presence of a Catholic prevents people from talking about religion while he is there, but ensures that they shall talk about it the moment that he has gone. No sooner was the front door shut than George said, 'I do wonder what Michael really thinks.'

'What about?' asked Margaret, bristling to Michael's defence before ever he was attacked.

'Oh, things,' said George.

'He's a Catholic, of course,' said Margaret. 'Didn't you know?'

'Oh, I know that he's a Catholic, of course,' said George. 'But what does he really think?'

'Oh, he believes it,' said Margaret. 'He told me he did.'

'But believes what?' said George. 'Really, Margaret, it's not quite as easy as all that. Suppose that he's on his way to Mass to-morrow, and he meets a pal. So instead of going to Mass they go to the pub and have a quick one . . .'

'The pubs would not be open,' put in Martin, speaking as an expert.

George, in the quest for truth, ignored the interruption. 'Supposing that he did . . .' he said.

'He'd be damned lucky if he got one from Armstrong,' said Martin.

'Well, as the result of having this drink, he was so late that he missed Mass. They have a definite rule about that, you know. Up to such-and-such a place it still counts that you have heard Mass and after that place you haven't heard it. I forget where the place is, but that does not matter. Anyway, he has missed Mass, so he is in mortal sin, and then, when he is coming away from Mass, he is knocked down by a car. Up till that morning he had lived a decent, edifying, pious life. Does Michael really believe that, if that happened to him, he would go to hell and burn through all eternity?'

'But they have a rule that you've got to go to Mass on a Sunday,' said Margaret, who was not quite following the point.

'Of course they have a rule,' said George, 'and a very sensible rule too. And, if a person breaks the rule, then he commits a sin. And if he commits a sin, then doubtless there must be some form or other of punishment. I have not got a word to say against all that. But how can they be so sure that it's a mortal sin? How can they know exactly the punishment that will follow? And can a reasonable, humane young man like Michael Paravane really believe that such a punishment is in proportion as an expression of the will of a loving God?'

'Well, it's an act of deliberate disobedience,' said Ruth.

'I remember when I was at school,' said Martin, 'that my housemaster told me not to visit other boys' rooms during prep. And I did, and I got caught, and he gave me six of the best, and it hurt like hell. Well, that was an act of deliberate disobedience and a fair cop, and I had nothing against him for what he did, and I dare say that it was very good for me. But if he had told me that I had to burn for ever afterwards I should have thought it a bit steep.'

'I don't believe a fellow like Michael does really believe all that,' I put in. 'He says that these are material mortal sins, and one only really commits a mortal sin if one does these things with a deliberate intention of defying God by doing it. I have not got it quite clear, but it's something like that.'

'That's better in a way,' said George, 'but logically it makes it all even more confusing. It's a first puzzle how intelligent and humane men can want to set out this exact rigmarole of legalistic detail of what exactly constitutes a mortal sin. But it's a further puzzle why they want to do this, if at the end of it all they are not even going to believe in it themselves. It's a perfectly reasonable proposition to say that a man whose life is a deliberate defiance of God goes to hell. It's not very different from what I believe myself, and of course he may defy God in breaking these various rules just as he may defy Him in any other way. But if the mortality of the sin is in the defiance, why not clearly say so, and why catalogue a whole list of detailed sins that obviously are normally committed without any wish at all to defy God?'

'But, George,' I protested, remembering past conversations, 'I thought that you were pro-hell—said that one could not get away from it, that there were some pretty tough things in the New Testament.'

'Oh, I'm pro-hell,' said George, 'if you mean by that that

I am not willing, in view of the New Testament, to go on record that nobody goes to hell. But the things that Christ speaks of people going to hell for seem to bear no resemblance to these legalistic rules which the Roman Church lays down.'

'Tell me, George,' I said, for his words were delivered in all the tone of a man engaged upon a personal argument, 'did you ever think of becoming a Roman Catholic?'

'No,' he said, 'I don't know that I did. Or rather,' he added after lighting a cigarette, 'the Roman Catholic Church has played such an enormous part in history that every intelligent person must, I suppose, at some time or other in his life consider whether her claims are not true, but I can fairly say that I was never bitten by them.'

'But why not?' asked Ruth. 'It's not like you to be just anti-things.'

'Oh, I'm not anti-Catholic in the sense of wanting to go and throw stones at their statues,' said George. 'If Michael Paravane is really satisfied where he is, I would not say a word to unsettle him. Indeed, if somebody came to me and said that he wanted to go over to Rome, I should only ask him to be quite sure that he had really made up his mind before he took such a step.'

'And what about mixed marriages?' asked the interested Margaret.

'Well, since that's the rule that they make that the children have to be brought up Catholics, you've got to accept it if you want to marry a Catholic. That's all there is to it.'

'We've got to accept it,' said Ruth; 'but I can't see that it's fair.'

'Oh, it's quite fair on their premises,' said George. 'We don't pretend that the Church of England is the whole of the Christian Church, so to us it can only be a secondary matter whether a child is brought up in one branch of the

Church or another. But to them theirs is the whole of the Church that Christ founded, which makes things quite different.'

'But I don't understand you, George,' said Ruth. 'Why do you say that they are reasonable if you don't agree with them?'

'Oh, well, a person can be quite reasonable on his own premisses,' said George. 'If you argue on Roman lines you quite reasonably reach Roman conclusions. Christ founded a Church against which the gates of Hell should not prevail. Where, then, is it to-day? It must be somewhere. *Scindi non potest.* It cannot possibly be anywhere but in the Roman Church. *Ubi Petrus, ibi ecclesia.*'

'What about Anglo-Catholics?' I asked.

'Oh no,' said George. 'If you want a Church like the Roman Catholic Church you had much better have the Roman Catholic Church. The Romans have no great difficulty in making nonsense of branch theories and Anglican claims to Apostolic Succession and all that. But supposing that one puts the whole argument differently?'

'How?' I asked. I always have had a genuine curiosity to know how arguments run, and I must confess to my shame that I, like most educated Englishmen, had reached middle age without any more than the haziest of notions how educated men defended the main theological positions.

'Well,' said George, 'I would argue that Christ was indeed God and that He did indeed found a Church, but as for the detailed organisation of that Church we know very little, and we have no reason at all to think that Christ held the details of that organisation to be of the first importance. On the other hand, He did promise "By their fruits ye shall know them," and "Where two or three are gathered together in My name, there am I in the midst of them." Well, if we look at the world to-day and over the last two thousand years, I think that we can say that, for all their shortcomings and for all that Bert may argue, there is a definite superiority of Christians over non-Christians. But can anybody seriously say that there is a superiority of Catholics over Protestants? Maybe that the Catholics are rather better; maybe that they are rather worse. It is my honest opinion that, if you take them on any ordinary test such as that of common honesty, they are rather worse. But, if you like, say that that is just my prejudice. Say that there is nothing much to choose between Catholics and Protestants, but no one can honestly think that they have this marked superiority over Protestants which one would expect if they were the unique recipients of revelation and of grace. It is this unique claim that I object to. I think that Christ is, as He promised, present whenever two or three are gathered together in His name. In that way He has been present, and is present, with devout and saintly Romans, of whom there are certainly many. But He has also been present with many other sincere Christians who are not Romans. I think that the Church is the body of all sincere believers and that Christ is, as He promised, with all those who sincerely confess Him. "What think ye of Christ? Whose Son is He?" seems to me the crucial text.'

'But what about the Petrine text?' said Ruth.

'The common-sense interpretation of that surely is that Christ will build His Church on the rock of the confession that He is the Christ, the Son of the Living God. He will build it on Peter so far as Peter had made that confession, but it seems to me a twisting of the plain sense to find in these words that extraordinary personal claim for Peter—and still more of a twist to extend the claim to Peter's successors.'

I usually found George's theological arguments very convincing. This was partly because he was both a holier and a more learned man than I and partly, of course, because he had spent a lifetime in thinking on these matters, which had unfortunately been but rarely in my mind, and therefore the crude difficulties which seemed to me so original were all entirely familiar to him. He was impatient with them, not because there were no difficulties but because these did not touch the real difficulties. I was interested to find that George could put up what seemed to me an entirely reasonable scriptural case against the Catholic claims.

'From my point of view,' said George, 'the supremely important thing is to believe in the Divinity of Christ. There must necessarily be a difference from A to Z on every opinion on the nature of the universe or the destiny of man between a person who believes that there was this extraordinary Divine intervention in human history and a person who does not believe it. Therefore, although I do not believe a lot of the other things that it says, I am with the Roman Church in what both it and I agree to be the most important point of all—an uncompromising stand on the full claim for the Divinity of Our Lord. But I am against it in so far as it makes it more difficult for intelligent people to accept that claim by tying it up with legalistic teachings that are untenable.'

'Well, you can take each thing on its merits?' said Ruth.

'No, but that's just what you can't do,' said George, 'on Catholic teaching—or at least on my understanding of it. You have to take the whole menu *table d'hôte*. That is just why I should be so interested to discover what Michael Paravane really believes. But my understanding is that the Church says to him, "I have authority to teach, and I teach that Jesus Christ was the Son of God and that people who have a little bacon for their breakfast on Friday go to hell and that people who repeat certain words in a certain place get off so many days in purgatory, and you, Michael Paravane, have to accept all this without picking and choosing. And if you don't accept any of it, then you're not a

Catholic." That seems to me to increase the difficulty of accepting the facts that are important and that have a whole lot of serious evidence in their favour.'

'How do you decide what's important?' asked Margaret.

'The Apostles' Creed seems to decide for one very satisfactorily,' said George. 'After all, what else are Apostles for?'

This, as I say, all seemed to me quite sensible. Yet I did feel that the devil's advocate must have a say and, indeed, that his client's case was worth hearing.

'Now, George,' I broke in, 'just a minute. You talk as if there were a number of Christian bodies—the Roman Catholics, the Church of England and the rest—all agreeing with one another in accepting the Divinity of Christ but differing on other points—all the members of each of the bodies truly believing all the formularies of his particular denomination. But you know it isn't like that in the least.'

'I never said it was,' said George. 'I started off by asking what Michael Paravane really believed.'

'Yes,' I said, 'but let's ask what some other people really believe, too! You say that Roman Catholic laymen only believe because their priests tell them to, but I answer with the much more serious charge that Protestant laymen only believe in spite of the fact that their priests tell them not to.'

'Oh,' said George. 'I really cannot recall an occasion when you displayed a passionate anxiety to accept the doctrines of the Christian religion and I urged you not to.'

'Oh, George,' I said, 'don't be a damned fool. I'm not talking about you personally. I am talking generally—and seriously. I think that there are all sorts of decent men and women scattered over the country who are anxious to believe and ready to believe and think that the whole non-Christian scheme has broken down and who look up to the clergy to lead them. And then what happens? A man like Hensley Henson, who has held almost the highest position that it is possible to hold in the Church, who is probably the best writer of English prose alive to-day, writes his autobiography. And in it he says what fools all the people who believe in traditional Christianity are, that he's agnostic about the Virgin Birth, and that he does not think that there is any evidence that Christ instituted the Eucharist. Well, if the Bishop of Durham says it's all boloney, it does not make it exactly easier for the rest of us to believe.'

'Yes, that's a fair point as far as it goes,' said George. 'But I never argued that the Church of England, as such, was part of the Church of Christ. I have never seriously pretended that I belonged to the Church of England through anything more than an accident of birth or owed to it much more loyalty than one might owe to the school one was at. I said that the Church of Christ comprehended all sincere believers, and that you could find such sincere believers in every denomination, and doubtless in every denomination could find people who did not believe.'

'Yes, but supposing that the Roman Catholics could say that at least they had a machinery which prevented people from attacking these central doctrines from their pulpits. Might they not argue that that machinery was part of the Divine plan?'

'Oh, the Roman Catholics have had their Modernists, too,' said George. 'There was the Abbé Loisy.'

'Don't cheat, George,' I said. 'For God's sake don't cheat. It's not worth while talking if one cheats. Of course Loisy did not believe, but then Loisy was excommunicated. But Henson was not excommunicated. He was made a bishop and there was apparently nothing that anybody could do about it.'

'All right,' said George, 'but what, then, about Talleyrand or some of the eighteenth-century French bishops, or the Renaissance Popes—who said that Christianity was a profitable superstition for Popes?'

'How many Renaissance Popes said that?' I asked. 'Did they all say it one after the other? It does not sound very probable. Still, I grant that you have more of a point there. It is just a question of history what these men really did say or believe. I don't pretend to be learned enough to know about that. I only know what people say about them in fifth-hand gossip—which is a very different thing. But even if all your accusations are true, they are not quite a case in point. For if these men were really sceptics, then they were also cynics. They frankly confessed that they preached one thing and believed another. They did not pretend that not believing in Christianity was a new and purified form of Christianity. The scandal about Hensley Henson is that he is so clearly a good and sincere man. It would be far less shocking if he were just a cynical adventurer.'

George got up from his chair and walked over to the bookshelf by the window. He stood with his back to us looking at the books for some minutes. Then he turned round and said to me:

'I think you have got an obviously sincere point there, Peter, and it is almost blasphemous to try to answer points like that in some single crisp sentence that would do for shutting up a heckler at a meeting, even if I could think of such a sentence. Obviously there are all sorts of things wrong with the rest of us, but two blacks do not make a white, and our sins do not alter my opinion that the legalisms of the Roman system are a stumbling-block to faith. Perhaps they have too much discipline and we have too little and the truth lies in a happy mean. I do not know. I do not pretend to be able to give a simple answer.'

'Something between

Send him flying
Off to hell, a Manichee

and

Pish—
He's a good fellow—and 'twill all be well.

I said a little irreverently.

'If you like to put it that way,' said George.

George's mind was possessed of a peculiarly admirable and honest quality. I have never known him for the sake of a debater's victory to take advantage of an opponent's weakness or confusion, to pretend an answer to a difficulty which he did not honestly feel himself capable of answering. He never made any pretence that all the mysteries of God were an open book entirely ready for his reading. After such an answer it did not seem fair to press him further. But Martin was roused by the mention of the bishops to the venting of a somewhat typical young man's grievance.

'The point we all want to get clear is this . . .' he began.

'Who's we?' I asked.

'The younger generation,' he said.

'Good God!' I answered, fearing the worst—indeed, as it proved, worse than was to come.

'It's about sex,' he said.

'It would be,' said Ruth.

'No, seriously, Mummy darling, do listen,' said Martin. 'The whole Christian tradition has been that sexual instincts are to be treated quite differently from other instincts. With other instincts Christian teaching gives only the most general guidance and leaves us largely to settle for ourselves what is right and wrong. On sex it has always been very much more explicit. It has told us exactly what we may and may not do in particular cases. Well, seeing the very explicit things that Our Lord has to say in the Gospels about divorce and adultery, that is not unreasonable. It is quite a reasonable proposition to say that these matters have been settled by direct Divine command and that therefore we are not free to make up our minds about them. But once the bishops start saying, as they did say at the Lambeth Conference, that changed circumstances have made certain practices right that all Christians used to think were wrong, then they can no longer pretend that they are expounding the law of God. They are expressing their own opinions, and, opinion for opinion, there is no reason why a bishop's should be better than anybody else's. Well, here we all are—living under exceptionally difficult circumstances in a non-Christian world and with every temptation to do as the non-Christians around us do. We have just a chance of keeping something like straight if we are given clear Christian teaching. But if the teaching is itself confused, what hope is there that our conduct will be better than that of our neighbours?'

'You can't pretend that the bishops have ever approved of free love,' said George.

'Of course they have not approved of free love,' said Martin. 'When they see the goings-on in the world, they get up on their hind legs and denounce them. But it never seems to occur to them how great is their share of responsibility for those goings-on by having weakened people's faith in the Law of God. After all, if marriage is not a sacrament, it is difficult to see how it is not merely a fetish. Doubtless it is a convenience to have some sort of a contract about the terms on which a man and woman live together, just as one would have some sort of contract about the terms on which one would rent a house, but there is no very obvious reason why, if unions are merely for convenience, then it is not sometimes convenient to have them irregular.'

'Oh, there's something to be said for monogamy on purely social grounds, quite apart from religion,' I said.

'Yes, something to be said for it,' said Martin, 'and something to be said against it. But the question is whether there is enough to be said for it to make it at all likely that people will behave themselves at moments of temptation if they don't believe that there are clear religious sanctions.'

'Most people complain that the bishops have not moved enough with the times,' said George.

'And most people are quite right,' said Martin, 'because if they move at all and agree to any revision of the traditional Christian teaching, then they have forfeited their right to interfere anywhere and are just Mrs. Grundys if they object to anything.'

'Everyone believes these days except the bishops and the writers in the *New Statesman*,' I said.

'Quite a good crack, Peter,' said George. 'But, you know, alas! that it is not true. Do you think that there is less of all this among the Roman Catholics, where the bishops have made no concessions?'

'I don't know if there is or if there isn't,' said Martin. 'Obviously sinners sin everywhere. But if you are taught that the code is something outside yourself, then you have a chance of pulling yourself together. But if you are taught that you can make up for yourself what is right and wrong then you have absolutely no chance. You have nothing to fight with.'

'What they used to call moral disarmament,' I said.

'Exactly,' said Martin.

'The Roman Catholics are frightfully detailed about exactly what constitutes a sin of sex,' said George, 'and frightfully vague about what constitutes any of the other sins of the flesh. I do not know if it is the result of the legislators being celibates.'

'Oh, they say that there are other sins besides those of sex,' said Margaret.

'Yes,' said George, 'there is such a thing as a mortal sin of drunkenness, but if you read up the conditions of it you will find that only the very ablest theologians have any chance of committing it! But I agree that our bishops ought to stick to the traditional teaching, just as I agree that they ought to leave people reasonable freedom on points on which there is not any traditional teaching.'

The conversation seemed to be in danger of completing its circle and coming back again to George's King Charles' Head of the legalism of the moral theologians. It was prevented from doing so by Bertha's cheery entry with a laden tray and a 'Now then, Mr. Borthwick, can I get to the table, please?'

Obviously Martin's real interest was in the problems of pre-marriage rather in those of marriage. As such, all that he said was honourable, while George's standpoint was the only one that could decently be taken by a Christian clergyman. Yet I could not think the problem quite as simple as they made it out to be. I entirely agree that the general law of society must be one of monogamy, that it is a grave and unfair handicap for children to have divorced parents, that those who have married are under obligation to make every effort to bring their marriage to success rather than to throw it up at the first difficulty. I agree that Christ has apparently laid upon His followers a special command forbidding divorce. Yet one has to deal with the actual situations as one finds them. It was all very well for Martin to say that the laws of God must be unchanging. There was a sense in which he was quite right. Nevertheless, new circumstances do to some extent create new conditions. It is one thing to legislate in a world in which a single marriage is the rule. It is another to legislate in a world in which, as the present, it is rapidly becoming almost the exception.

It may be said that it is a mistake that the divorce laws

should be so free and that society would be the happier were there less divorce. I have little doubt that this is so, but it does not touch my point—my doubt what should be done with things as they are. I was thinking, for instance, of Tony Arbuthnot. Tony, as I have already said, had been divorced and was now living with his third wife, a very decent chorus-girl, with whom he seemed to be getting on tolerably well. They had two little children who were growing up in a happy family atmosphere.

Then Tony, who was a creature of sudden whims, had—I know not why—the whim to become a Roman Catholic. Nothing could have been more surprising, but the rummiest people do suddenly get the whim to become Roman Catholics. He went along to see a priest, and the priest, of course, said to him that he could not be received unless he broke with his present marriage. His duty was to return to his first—his real—wife. But this was hardly possible, as she had subsequently made her way through two more husbands and was now living with a Bolivian tin-merchant in Buenos Aires. Tony was by now in the complicated position of owning five children, divided up among three separate wives. He argued with the priest, 'You preach the sanctity of marriage, and you demand that a marriage should be broken up. You say that it is the worst thing in the world for children to be brought up without family life, and you are demanding that a family be scattered just on a technicality.' The priest said something or other about in certain circumstances husband and wife being allowed to live together as brother and sister. But the mere suggestion of this sent Tony off into a fit of laughter. Then the priest said that he was very sorry, but there was nothing that he could do about it, and, though I do not know very much about Catholic theology, I suppose that there was nothing else that he could have said. 'It's not that I think you a bad man,' explained the priest, so Tony told me. '"I should think not," I answered,' said Tony. '"I'm a good man, leading a good life under exceptionally difficult circumstances."'

So Tony went off and got drunk and ten days later he had forgotten that there ever was such a thing as the Roman Catholic Church. 'I joined something else instead,' he told me. 'I forget now what.'

It seems quite logical, in view of Christ's words, that a Christian should be forbidden to divorce his wife, but when he has already divorced her and married another and had a family by a second wife, surely here is an actual situation existing here and now, and, as Tony put it with some force, 'one cannot very well just tell the children of the second marriage that they are a lot of bastards and turn them out into the street.' Frankly I do not know the answer. I entirely see the strength of Martin's argument that, if the bishops do not stand on the Divine law, then there is nowhere for them to stand at all. But I also entirely see the strength of Tony's argument that a family exists and that it is not helpful merely to say that it ought not to have existed. Tony, of course, solved the problem, as most people would solve such a problem, by rejecting and neglecting the Christian religion, but to one who thinks the Christian religion true that cannot be a satisfactory solution. Ruth, who had no great love for Tony, said that the Catholics were well rid of him. But this was a woman's comment—and not a very worthy one. The laws of God and man were made for the sake of Tony as for the rest of us. Tony, with all his faults, was not one of those whom Bobby used to describe by saying, 'They haven't got a sake.' And even if it be true that Tony's religious fervour would not have persisted for very long in any event, there are many others as entangled as he and with the deeper nature that needs a spiritual home.

A better argument was that of Tony's cousin, Marigold

Arbuthnot, who said that it was no unfortunate accident that Tony's marriages never worked. A marriage entered into by Tony, she argued, could not of its nature work. 'If you embark upon matrimony purely as a form of self-indulgence, it is certain to prove an unsatisfactory form of self-indulgence. You can't argue against marriage from looking at modern marriages of that sort,' said Marigold. 'If you turn the switch and the light does not go on, you have reason to believe that there is something wrong with the light, but you can't blame the switch if you have not turned it, and Tony would be more of an authority on the difficulties of fidelity if he had ever tried it.'

I remembered how my father, although he was not a particularly religious man, used to hold his dead wife's picture in his hands throughout his last long, painful illness, and Marigold's point seemed to me to be a just one.

XV

I HATE snow. Even when I was a boy I used to hate it. Skating and tobogganing have never had for me a sufficient attraction to compensate for the cold damp of ice and snow on the fingers. The whole winter world is to me a badger world, sleeping and waiting for the resurrection of spring's first breath. But snow, if it must be, is best at a distance, and the sun of winter, if it cannot warm, can at any rate illuminate. The roads and valleys were dry and brown when a few days later Margaret and I set out to bicycle over to Hinton Charity; the little touch of snow of the day before had not lain there, but the line of it still tipped the height of the Mendips to the eastern horizon, and the pale sun that had just struggled above them picked it out like a line of life.

Margaret and I packed ourselves some sandwiches and got off at about half-past eleven, planning to reach Hinton Charity after lunch. Margaret was a cyclist of the absurd school, which still flourishes among the young, liking to take both hands off the handle-bars just to show that she could. She also had that frightful feminine habit of not being thirsty in the middle of the day. She would alternately loiter intolerably and rush forward at a break-neck speed. I was a cyclist, avuncular—a stern and steady pedaller. Our journeys were therefore conducted in an atmosphere of unabating controversy, but it was a light-hearted controversy, enlivened by jokes which, if too inane for repetition, were at least sufficient to while away the tedium of a road that wound uphill almost all the way.

Margaret was contemptuous of my contempt of snow.

'But don't you feel a tang in the air which makes you want to shout on a day like this?' she asked me as I found her waiting, patient but champing, at the foot of a hill which she had descended with brakeless precipitancy.

'No, I'm too old,' I said, and I had a sudden, stabbing, horrid knowledge that what I said was true.

We reached Hinton Charity at a little after half-past two. In many ways the house was a sad place these days. The drive swept in up a little hill through what used to be some not ignoble iron gates. These had now gone for the needs of munitions, leaving only the stone gate-posts—and nothing in the world looks quite as silly as gate-posts without any gates. The hard tennis court was now a derelict wilderness, and the south court, whose lawn was the boast of three hundred years, was given up to spinach and potato. Michael always repudiated that gastronomic puritanism which alleges that flowers are unnecessary because they are inedible. In spite of every demand, he contrived that a blaze of azalea and rhododendrons of various kinds should fill his garden from the end of March until midsummer, and he boasted that if ever Hitler landed there should be the red rose and the white rose proud to meet him. But what good could these boasts do to dissipate the desolation of late December? There was an atmosphere as of the valley of desolation about the place.

The black troops who had occupied it a year before had now gone, and in their stead it had been turned into an officers' mess. But I do not really know that the change was an improvement. God knows that I am no æsthete and no highbrow, but there comes a point where lack of culture becomes almost terrifying. Michael had a few quite decent Neroccios or pseudo-Neroccios—nothing much perhaps, but there they were. He wisely did not leave these to the officers' mercy, but hung them in a little parlour in the small corner of the rambling house which he was allowed to keep for his own use. The officers broke into this parlour one evening after dinner, when Michael was away. They found a pot of paint and with its aid put a pipe into the mouth of St. Francis of Assisi in one picture and spectacles on to the noses of the Three Wise Men in another. They signed their names across St. Sebastian's body. They were men of liberal opinions. 'Fancy things like these,' they argued with Michael when he spoke to them on the matter, 'should not belong just to one rich man. They should belong to the community.' 'Yes, everybody should share,' said the adjutant as he finished off Michael's last bottle of Madeira, to which he had helped himself before the commanding officer should have time to get his whack.

Michael had been brought up by his father at a little villa which they owned at Certaldo in Southern Tuscany—the place where Boccaccio is buried. No memories are so vivid as those of boyhood, and I know that the chaffering contadini, the slow-moving oxen, the happy, grubby, laughing Tuscan children, San Gimignano of the Lovely Towers, seen across the valley, like a city in a missal, or the Duomo of Siena from Fontebranda, the olives blown to silver in the wind and the grapes kissed to purple and gold by sunshine —these were never long from his mind. No man was ever less of a Fascist than he, but one only judges people whom one does not know by their politics. When one knows better one judges by more important tests, and it was thus that he judged the Italians. The tragedy, the agony that we should have had to fight them, the doubt whether our culture was strong enough to survive such an unnatural breach, were ever present to him. The adjutant had no such doubts.

'The Italians,' he explained, 'are degraded. Men can't be happy when they're degraded.'

He pronounced the word 'can't' with a short 'a'—like the German philosopher—which was, I must say, extraordinarily unattractive.

A temper less equable than that of Michael Paravane would have resented the vigour with which his guests ruined his property, drank his precious drinks and denounced him as a parasite of privilege. But Michael had a curiously invincible belief in democracy, which survived even the company of democrats. So firm was his faith in human equality that he even believed that officers were the equals of their men, and he believed also that these appalling officers, though they did not deserve to be right, yet were right when they preached the common rights of beauty. He thought that impatience was the great evil and that in time men would come to know and love that from which they were not debarred. The generality, he insisted, even of officers was not so bad, and if ill chance brought to one's door men of such a nature it was folly to waste time in too much complaining at that which could not be avoided.

When Margaret and I visited Michael, we always played billards. Michael and I used to play while Margaret sat and watched. Margaret's curiosity had clearly been aroused by George's dissertations, and, indeed, if she was to become Michael's wife and if her children were to be brought up in Michael's faith, then she had some right to a satisfaction of her curiosity.

Michael was stringing for the right to break when Margaret broached the question. She broached it in a fashion characteristic of her.

'Michael,' she said, 'do you think that I would go to hell if I ate a sausage for breakfast on a Friday?'

'Of course not,' said Michael. 'Why should you? You're in invincible ignorance. People in invincible ignorance can eat as many sausages as they like—or at least as many as they can get.'

'Well, then,' persisted Margaret, 'do you think that you would go to hell if you ate a sausage for breakfast on a Friday?'

'Ah, now you're coming nearer the bone,' said Michael. 'But then one out of the many examples of the invincibility of your ignorance is that you have not realised that we don't have to abstain on Fridays in war-time.'

'Oh, well, suppose that there wasn't a war?' she asked.

'Ah, well,' said Michael, 'suppose that there wasn't a war and suppose that there was some meat in a sausage—what a lot of things we do have to suppose, don't we?'

I thought, I must confess, that Michael was being a bit silly. I put down my cue, and, turning round to him, said, 'Look here, I honestly think that you owe Margaret a sensible answer to her question. It may be that the rest of us have not the right to press you to tell us what your beliefs are, and, if you like, I will leave the room, but, if you expect Margaret to become your wife one day, then I think that you ought to confess them to her.'

'Leave the room sooner than listen to me delivering a lecture on moral theology with a billiard cue as a pointer?' said Michael. 'My dear Peter, how can you possibly bring yourself to suggest such a thing? But with the profoundest respect to the lady who has done me the great honour to say that she will become my wife, how can I give a sensible answer to a question to which I do not know the answer?'

'Well, it seems to me quite a fair question,' I said. 'Your Church teaches that you go to hell if you eat meat on a Friday, and George says that he doesn't believe that a person like you really can hold such a doctrine. It seems quite a fair question to ask what you really do believe.'

'Quite a fair question,' said Michael, throwing himself into a chair and lighting a cigarette, 'and I have given you quite a fair answer. I don't know. I believe that my Church has laid down for me certain rules of conduct and that it will be the better for me if I keep those rules and the worse for me if I break them. But what precise offences will qualify for what precise punishments and what the punishments will exactly mean I don't know. There's nothing that you agnostics don't know, and you're always ready to explain exactly what the God who may not exist will do under every sort of hypothetical circumstance. But I'm just a believer. I don't know.'

'I'm not an agnostic,' I protested; 'at least, not exactly. And, anyway, George certainly is not an agnostic. George is quite prepared to think that people whose whole life is turned away from God will go to hell, but he says that it's absurd to imagine that anyone will go to hell just for a single legalistic offence like that.'

Michael burst out laughing.

'Well, that's damned decent of George,' he said; 'but, after all, will he be running the Last Judgment? I mean to say—supposing that I turn up at the Last Judgment in a state of mortal sin and say to Almighty God, "Oh, George said it wouldn't matter so much"—well, you know, there's just a chance that it might not go down too well. There's just a chance that God might answer, "Who's George?"—only I suppose that He would know, because He knows everything—and then I should look a pretty fair fool. And so, with profound respect, I prefer not to take a chance on what George says if I can possibly avoid it.'

'I do wish you would be serious, Michael,' said Margaret.

'I am, darling, being profoundly serious,' said Michael. 'Every now and again one comes across a priest who spins out some theory which tries to show that as few people as possible will go to hell. Well, I always felt that those theories prove that the priest is a very kindly and decent fellow, but they do not prove very much more. To tell the truth, I'm not so very interested in what all sorts of other people would do if they were God. I am interested in what God will do.'

'But surely,' I said, 'you can't believe that a loving God would damn people?'

'You may be right, Peter,' said Michael. 'I'm not saying that you aren't right for a moment. I hope to God that you are right. I'm simply saying that I don't know. You see, I just don't happen to be God.'

'You're fencing, Michael,' said Margaret.

'I'm not fencing, darling,' said Michael. 'I'm deadly serious. Whether nobody knows the answer to these questions or whether some very learned and very holy men alone know them it is not for me to say. All that I say for myself is that I just don't know. I think that one of the most important things is to understand that life is wrapped round with mystery and that we know very little, and that we shall soon get into a mess if we start trying to answer questions that we cannot answer. What ordinary people need to do is to live by a code without asking too many questions. Naturally I think that the code by which I try to live is the best of all codes, but even if it wasn't the best code it would be the hell of a lot better to live by it than to live by no code at all. I am not boasting that I succeed or that I shall succeed. I am telling you what I will try to do. Is that an answer, darling?' And he took Margaret's hand in his and leant forward and kissed her.

'Now may I play billiards, please?' he said.

'All right, you can play billiards now,' she said, laughing.

We had our game while Margaret sat silent and smoking on the settee. It was always one of Michael's major theses that it was a sign of the mental decline of the age that it should be considered unsporting to pot the white, and when the score was ninety-eight to him and eighty-three to me he unhesitatingly finished it off by sinking me in the top left-hand pocket. My appeals to him to behave like a gentleman went scornfully unheeded.

Margaret was still pensively chain-smoking on the settee.

'Yes, but, Michael,' she said, as we put the cues away, 'why do you think that it is the best code?'

'What?' said Michael absently, 'potting the white? Why, it's common sense if there's nothing else that you can do. What is there to be said against it?'

'No, not potting the white, you idiot,' said Margaret. 'The Roman Catholic Church.'

'Oh, the Church,' said Michael. 'Good God, are we back on that? This is a session. Well, we must have a drink before we come to that.'

He poured out three large and rare whiskeys in honour of the death of the Old Year.

'Well, then, shoot,' he said, sipping. 'What is the point now?'

'Well, why is it you believe it all?' asked Margaret.

'Oh, I was brought up that way,' he said.

'But you must have more reason than that,' she said.

'I think it's a very good reason,' he said. 'Much better than the reason why most people believe in things—just because they've read them in the newspapers.'

'Still, that's a quibble,' I said. 'You have more reason than that.'

Michael frowned a little and took another generous sip of his whiskey.

'Yes,' he said, 'I suppose that that's fair. I suppose that I have.'

'Well, do tell us what it is,' I said. 'What is there to be so shy of?'

'Oh, I don't know,' said Michael. 'It's all so unco-ordinated—exactly the opposite of a Newman's *Apologia* or a Thomist *Summa*. For instance, a few weeks ago I met Carruthers in the road the day after he had heard about his son going down on that destroyer. It was dreadful. I tried to mutter something, and he said, "Yes, a bad show—a bad show." Then he tried to talk about the crops, and he broke down in the middle with a great gulp and looked away. At last he pulled himself together and just managed to finish the sentence. "I'm sorry," he said. "I'm so sorry. It's very foolish. Thank you so much." Then he left me. I had seen his eyes behind the tears and he was suffering like hell.'

'Yes,' I said, 'it was all terribly sad. They were both frightfully proud of that boy, and he was their only one. But what on earth has this got to do with the truth of Catholicism? Carruthers is not a Catholic.'

Carruthers was in fact the local rector—anything but a Catholic.

'Of course he is not a Catholic, you ass!' said Michael. 'Do you think I don't know that?'

'Well,' I said, 'I don't follow your point then.'

'My point is this,' said Michael. 'Sometimes we have a feeling that death is really the end, that materialism is all and that everything else is sentimentality and wishful-thinking. And, of course, with ninety-nine people out of a hundred, we read of their deaths in the paper, and say, "How sad," and drop a line of sympathy to their wives or parents and then go out and have a drink and never give the matter another thought. That's just what I would have done about Carruthers' son, if I had not happened to meet the old boy in the road. But then I saw from his eyes how much he was suffering, and I was haunted by that suffering. But at the same time it seemed to me that his suffering proved a whole lot. It showed a depth of love—an affection far deeper than could be accounted for by an accident of their having some tastes in common. Where had that love come from? And then the old boy, who is usually a bit grubby and down at heels, seemed to have taken on a strange dignity through having come into contact with death. People do, you know. Death, whatever it is, is dignified. It's not just ridiculous. It's something entirely different from a motor-car breaking down. All pride slips away from people when they are face to face with death. It's a very wonderful thing to see a man quite without pride. A man's death is even something quite different from an animal's death. "*Animula, vagula, blandula.*" Why should people ever doubt materialism, if materialism was true? And then Carruthers' suffering had another odd effect on me. I felt it absolutely intolerable, if I could not somehow manage to suffer with him too. What was the sense of that? And I could not imagine what to do. I muttered again how sorry I was, but by that time the old boy was stumbling off down the road and did not hear. So I could not pretend that that had done any particular good. What could I do? The only alternatives seemed to be to stand him a drink or to run after him and tell him "about the hope of a joyful resurrection." And neither the one nor the other seemed somehow quite right. So what I did do was to go home and then to go into our little church and say a prayer for him. I don't know if it did him any good, but it certainly did me a lot of good. And I must say that next time I met the old boy he seemed to have pulled himself together a good deal. But I don't say that *post hoc* was *propter hoc*.'

'But, Michael, what has this got to do with Catholicism?'

'A lot,' he said. 'The whole question is whether the scheme of things is sense or nonsense.'

'Well, a fellow like George would grant that the scheme of things—that is to say, the general scheme—was sense,' I said, 'but he would object to your people for laying so much stress on what he should call detailed legalisms.'

'Damn George and his bloody impudence,' said Michael, and burst out laughing. 'Has he ever read *Measure for Measure*?'

'I don't know if he has or not,' I said. 'I expect so. He has read most things.'

'Well, you tell George with my compliments, before he does any more talking, to sit down and read *Measure for Measure*,' said Michael. 'They never let me read it when I was at school—I suppose that they thought it too smutty—but it seems to me the ideal answer why anyone should be a Catholic.'

'Well, tell me all about it,' I said. 'I am ignorant and all attention.'

'It is rather a fantastic play, considered dramatically,' said Michael. 'The Duke of Vienna goes off into retirement and leaves power in the hands of his deputy, Angelo. Angelo launches out on an anti-vice campaign, and in the course of it a certain Claudio is to be executed for having been guilty of immorality. Isabella, Claudio's sister, who is a postulant nun, goes to Angelo to beg for her brother's life. Angelo, who, like so many Puritans, is a dirty old man under the skin, agrees to let Claudio off if Isabella will sleep with him. Isabella refuses this and says that, if that is the best that can be offered, then Claudio must die. Eventually they get out of it by a typically Shakespearean trick. Mariana, who had been married to Angelo by precontract and then jilted because she lost her dowry, disguises herself as Isabella and goes in to sleep with Angelo, Angelo imagining that he has been sleeping with Isabella. Then the Duke comes back, and everything ends in the usual Shakespeare Fifth Act. The Duke marries Isabella, and Angelo is very nearly executed but begged off by Mariana and Isabella, and goes off to live happily ever after in Mariana's moated grange, and Claudio has not been executed after all, so he is brought out of jug and set free and so on and so on.'

'It sounds to me a damned silly play,' I said.

'It is in many ways,' said Michael. 'But I am not concerned with the merits of the play. I am concerned with the particular point whether Isabella was right or wrong to refuse Angelo, though by her doing so her brother lost his life. All we moderns would be inclined to say that, whatever the general rights and wrongs about marriage and morality, yet Isabella obviously ought to have given in in this special case. But Shakespeare did not think so. Shakespeare and all the characters in the play, both the good and the bad, agree that Isabella was right, and that there was no sin being committed so long as Angelo slept with his wife, even if he did not know that it was his wife he was sleeping with. In the same way the moderns are inclined to say that it cannot make much difference whether a clergyman's orders are valid or not. But Shakespeare and Touchstone and Jacques in *As You Like It* clearly thought that it made all the difference whether Sir Oliver Martext was "a good priest." If he was, then Touchstone's marriage to Audrey was a marriage, and if he wasn't it was not a marriage. You say that it cannot make much difference whether a person confesses before his death or not. God's verdict cannot depend on an accident like that. But Shakespeare thought it made all the difference—to Hamlet's father and to Hamlet's uncle.'

'What does all that prove?' I asked.

'Well,' said Michael, 'simply that the modern mind thinks one thing but Shakespeare thought another. If you look round on the world you can hardly conclude that the modern mind has made much of a success of its thinking, while Shakespeare was a very intelligent man. I think that the odds are that Shakespeare was right and the modern mind is wrong.'

'But Shakespeare was not a trained moral theologian,' I said.

'Of course he was not,' said Michael; 'theologically he was a very ignorant and careless man. He gets all sorts of details about the sacraments wrong. I am not saying that you can use Shakespeare as a theological textbook. But what I do say is this. The modern view is that morals are all man-made—that we decide things to be right or wrong by looking to their probable consequences. Shakespeare's view is that things are right or wrong by a Divine law outside ourselves. If we obey the law the consequences will, as a general rule, be good—but not necessarily, as far as this world goes—and in any event it is not the consequences which make the actions right. Right is right, whatever the consequences. The world is an interpenetrated world. God is acting in it.'

'That's easy enough to say,' I objected, 'but do you really believe it, Michael? Have you ever seen it happening?'

'Of course I have,' he said. 'I saw it happening with old Carruthers. I just told you. But it's easier to see when it's not happening. When I was in Labrador a padre flew me out to look at a village of Eskimos. They had hardly ever seen a white man before. There they were at the end of nowhere in their dirty, primitive little huts, with the snow stretching out illimitably to the North Pole, and we went into their rough log chapel with smelly, smoking lamps. Well, I knelt there for benediction in front of the Blessed Sacrament and heard them singing *Tantum ergo sacramentum* out of their fur caps, and I reflected that I had nothing else in the whole world in common with these savages except the Blessed Sacrament, but that that was a thumping lot. Then I flew back to Montreal, and the next day I was sitting in the hotel there and seeing the rich men come in to eat and drink. Have you ever been in Montreal? God—it's a sight—rich men in Montreal. I don't see how anyone could ever see them and not believe in God. O God! O Montreal!'

'I'm afraid that I don't follow you, Michael,' I said.

'Don't you see that one feels the need for a thing by feeling the absence of it?' he said. 'Rich men in Montreal—it is not perhaps that any particular thing that they do is especially wicked, but their whole life is devoted to ends quite different from the ends for which they were made. There is a stamp of utter futility upon their every thought—the more successful the more futile. They had de-graded themselves in the most literal sense of the word—stepped themselves down a peg—turned themselves into a lower sort of being than they might have been and should have been. There is a whole atmosphere about them as of something having gone wrong. He "made them a little lower than the angels"—and—well—all I can say is that they are a whole hell of a lot lower after they have spent a lifetime in Montreal. One notices that when one's come straight from Eskimos, who at the worst never sink much lower than cannibalism.'

'I'm sorry to go on with the same point, but I still don't see what this has got to do with Catholicism in particular,' I objected.

'All right, I will tell you another story,' said Michael. 'When I was at Stonyhurst there was a boy there called Guillermo Echevaria. It was rather an absurd name and he was rather an absurd boy. None of us there ever did anything really wicked, as we came afterwards to count wickedness, but he was what, for a schoolboy, would count as a bad boy—always getting into scrapes and getting punished and being suspected (and, I dare say, justly) of telling lies and suchlike. Well, then, he went back to Mexico after he had left, and when I was in Mexico about eight years ago I went to see him. He made no attempt to conceal that he had developed much as one would have expected him to develop. The very possibility of chastity he scouted as "ridiculous." Nevertheless, he called himself a good, and indeed a keen, Catholic. His regimen was, as far as I gathered, to go with exemplary regularity to Mass, some three or four times a year to go to confession on a Saturday evening, accomplish the heroic feat of remaining out of mortal sin until the following morning, when he would piously receive Communion, and then very shortly afterwards he would start, as it were, again on his travels. Well, I'm not as continental as some people on these matters and cursed with an obstinate logical feeling that words mean what they say. (Why we say that the Latins are logical about their religion I cannot imagine.) I did not see how Guillermo could pretend that in his confessions he had either true sorrow for his sins or a firm purpose of amendment, and, that being so, I could not see how his confessions were good confessions and what was therefore the purpose of making them. But he did not at all take it like that. "Oh, I have an infirm purpose of amendment," he said laughingly, "and that is better than nothing. I should never dream of giving up Catholicism," he said. "Of course, I know damned well when I go to confession that I shan't remain chaste, but I have a vague sort of feeling that I should be a better man if I could be. The J's used to say that the sin that really mattered was pride. I look on incontinence as a kind of extension of original sin. One has to sin, but sin at least keeps one humble and prevents one from thinking that one's a fine fellow." '

'Rather like Luther, wasn't it?' I said.

'I don't know what it was like,' said Michael, 'but anyway it was obviously highly unorthodox and untenable. Nevertheless, I was rather impressed with the fact that, whatever sins he might commit, it had never occurred to him to twist theory to justify his conduct and abandon his faith. In a way I was more impressed than I would have been with someone who was completely flawless and holy. Had I found such a person I would have felt, "This is very wonderful and admirable, but he is obviously made quite differently from me." With Guillermo it was another story. There was something impressive about his loyalty in spite of his conduct. He was loyal through and through and in the most incongruous ways. I remember that he was holding forth one day about the superiority of Catholics over Protestants in the Catholic's freedom from race prejudice. "I once kept a black mistress," he said to me, triumphantly and seriously as a bull-point. "Now you know that there are plenty of Protestants who would call that wrong." '

I felt that here I had to interrupt Michael.

'I can't see anything particularly fine in all this, you know, Michael,' I said. 'Of course there are some Catholics who like to have the best of both worlds, and they pretend to be very humble by doing all sorts of things and then frankly confessing them. And then they jeer at us Protestants as prigs and prudes. But I must confess that I don't think such people either very admirable or very intelligent, and, when frankness is carried so far that the matter for private confession becomes matter for public boasting, then I cannot think their humility very real either. So far from being humble, I think that they are afflicted with a particularly odious sort of pride.'

'Perhaps,' said Michael. 'I'm not defending him. In fact, though in a way he impressed me, I rather disliked Guillermo. But that's not the point. The point is the sequel. Two years later they started up the religious persecution again in Vera Cruz, where Guillermo lived, and a few days after it had started the Director of Education, an illiterate little Indian about three foot six high, came to Guillermo's house with a posse of soldiers. Guillermo's brother, Francesco, whom I met shortly afterwards in Paris, told me what happened then. They wanted Guillermo, as a well-known Catholic, to say that he approved of the new scheme of sexual education in the schools. All the children were being taught that it was a good thing to have sexual experience and that chastity was impossible and bad for health. It was almost exactly what Guillermo himself had said to me two years before. But now, when the little half-breed Director of Education told him to say it, he answered, "No, I'm damned if I will." He had started off by asking him quite politely. Then, as the conversation went on, it got more and more violent—it was in the evening and they were both a little drunk, Guillermo on whiskey and the Director on pulque. At last the Director lost his temper and said, "If you don't say so, we'll shoot you, and you need not think that they will make a martyr of you like Father Pro, because we know very well that you were with a woman last night, and we'll see to it that everybody else knows, too. What's more, if we shoot you, you will go to hell too, because we won't let you have a priest." "A damned fine Director of Education you are," said Guillermo, "if you don't know that a soul can be saved even without confession if it has a perfect Christian disposition." And, suiting the action to the word, he let out a great kick and landed the little Director in the stomach.

The Director went down with a howl of rage and pain. Squirming on the floor, he shouted to his men to seize Guillermo and drag him out into the garden. They did so, and then they bound his legs and arms and gagged him. Then the Director came out into the garden and shouted out at him obscene blasphemies about Our Lady. People like that, you know, they not only are impure but they hate purity as an enemy .Then at the last he gave him a kick with his little foot and pulled out his revolver and emptied it into him. They left the body rotting there in the garden for days, and the loathsome black zopilote flew down and fed on it. A yellow dog came and sniffed round at its entrails. A negro servant who was hiding in the lavatory told all this to Francesco, and he told it to me.'

'That's a very striking story,' I said, 'but I really cannot see what it proves. In fact, quite honestly, I don't think that your reasons are particularly good reasons.'

'You didn't ask me for good reasons, Peter,' he said. 'You asked me for my reasons, which is quite a different thing. If you want to know the ordinary apologetic points about infallibility and transubstantiation and all the rest, you can come down with me one day to Parsons' Hall and see Father Custance. Or, if you like, I will even buy you a few twopenny pamphlets from the Catholic Truth Society. Everybody knows that there are answers on all these points, though I'm not particularly good at putting them and don't especially carry them in my head. But I thought that you wanted my personal reasons—a number of cumulative experiences of quite different kinds—no single one by itself conclusive—but in all of them the Catholic Church popping up, sometimes conspicuous by its presence and sometimes, oddly enough, even more conspicuous by its absence—the mark of things having something wrong about them when it is not there. You can't get away from it. It's like Christ in *The Hound of Heaven*. You go into the pub, and there you find it. You answer the telephone, and there it is.'

'I could see, if you said this about God or religion or even Christianity in general,' I said, 'but I cannot see why it's true of the Roman Catholic Church in particular. Is not that just as good a reason for joining the Church of England? You're allowed to believe in God there, too, you know. It's very Liberal.'

'Oh, George's show?' said Michael. 'Well, to tell the truth, I never heard of anybody joining that. I'm afraid that I never gave a thought to that to this moment. I don't pretend that that's a very sensible answer, but it's a truthful one.'

'I'm not sure that I have not joined it myself,' I said.

'You?' said Michael. 'I thought that you always were a member of a sort—a sort of non-paying, country member.'

'Oh yes, but I have moved a bit recently,' I said, 'but I don't know that it's towards you. It's more towards George, I think.'

'George is a very decent fellow,' said Michael. 'He gives one an answer when one asks him something. That is what the secularists never do. You used to be awful about that. You used to be a most frightful bloody fool, I must say, Peter, but you've been ever so much better since . . ."

He broke off the sentence very suddenly. I was intensely curious to know how he had proposed to finish it.

'Since what?' I asked.

'Oh, nothing,' he said.

'You can't play a trick like that, Michael,' I said. 'Once you've begun you must go on. Otherwise it's just tantalising.'

'No,' said Michael. 'I was going to say something quite unpardonably rude. I can't think how I ever dreamed of saying it.'

'What was it, anyway?' I asked.

'I will only tell you,' said Michael, 'if you promise to let me explain first before you explode.'

'All right,' I said. 'I promise.'

'Well, I was going to say,' said Michael, 'that you had become ever so much more sensible since your wife died. I did not mean by that, of course, to say a word in criticism of your wife. I merely meant to say that I thought that suffering had deepened you a whole lot, just as it does most people. And I do think that.'

'Yes, I think so too,' I said. 'I don't think that there is anything rude in that. I think that you're perfectly right.'

Margaret had slipped out for a minute during Michael's story of his friend's murder, and her absence had perhaps a bit eased the telling of it. I thought it only fair that she should have her innings now, and so went off to take a walk round the farm, leaving them together. When I returned it was time to be getting back, if we were to be home before black-out. We said good-bye, and Margaret and I mounted our bicycles. We rode for a time in silence, and then by the quarry we had to dismount to push up the hill.

'Your young man, my dear,' I said, leaning on the bicycle, 'he's a real top-notcher and you are very lucky to have landed him. But, you know, I can't in the last analysis quite understand his religion. I can understand a lot and see a lot of sense in it. But there is always something a bit more that I feel just escapes me. Do you feel that?"

'That's because of your anti-Catholic prejudice,' she said.

'Oh, no,' I answered. 'I haven't got any anti-Catholic prejudice. Rather the contrary. Of course I think that their position is fundamentally wrong.'

'Well, if you can't understand it and yet you think it wrong, I should have thought it quite fair to say that you had a prejudice,' said Margaret.

'No, I don't think so,' I replied, but I could see that she

was in no mood for implied criticisms of her affianced and let it drop.

'The particular arguments of Michael and Uncle George are quite different,' said Margaret, 'and I am not clever enough to judge between them. But they both have much the same effect on me. I feel that there is so much more that the world is about when I hear them talking than when other people talk. I'm afraid that I don't put it very well,' she added.

'On the contrary, my dear,' I answered, 'you put it admirably and I entirely agree with you.'

'But do you really believe it all, Peter?' she asked.

I thought a minute.

'I feel absolutely certain,' I answered, 'that something from beyond the world impinged into the world with the Christian religion. I have no doubt of that. Whether the Christian explanation of the impingement is the full one is another question. Sometimes its relations seem to me so anthropomorphic. I feel that there may be something more to it than all that.'

'But Christianity never claims that the creeds contain all truth,' Margaret said. 'It merely claims that they are all true as far as they go. Is not that good enough?'

'Perhaps,' I said. 'Frankly I don't know. I must think it out. I have a slow mind and I'm not going to be bounced, my dear—least of all by my own niece!'

At the top of the hill we came to the cross-roads and to the little church of Whatley. The joyless December evening was closing down. A trickle of light peered out from the as yet unblacked-out windows, and someone was inexpertly practising on the organ. It is not a whim that often comes to me, but I suddenly thought that I would like to look in at the church. I made the suggestion to Margaret.

'Why?' she asked.

'I have no idea,' I said. 'I just thought of it.'

'Oh, all right, so long as you don't have a theory about it,' she said. 'But don't let's be too long.'

The hymn-books lying about, the list of vicars, the hassocks, the Ten Commandments, the trailing pussy bell-rope—there was indeed nothing to keep us long within the building, and I was soon out again. I was out before Margaret, who stopped to speak a word with the organist, and, waiting for her, I stood gazing at the tomb of Dean Church, who was for many years Whatley's Rector and came to be buried there at last, far from the busy pulpit of St. Paul's. The words of the old mediæval hymn, inscribed on the tomb, stood out at me,

Rex tremendæ maiestiætis,
Qui salvandos salvas gratis,
Salva me, fons pietatis.

'Who was Dean Church?' asked Margaret, who had come up behind me.

'He was a man who wrote very good prose about the Oxford Movement,' I said.

'And what was the Oxford Movement,' she persisted.

'Well, my dear,' I said, 'it was something that was not invented by Dr. Buchman. That was by far the most important thing about it, and, incidentally, I am afraid, almost the only thing that I know.'

It was indeed true that I knew extremely little about Dean Church, but at least, I reflected, I knew this much. He was a more learned, a more intelligent and a more holy man than I was or than were any of the rest of us who so easily laughed off our fears of a Judgment. For every minute that I had spent meditating on these things he had doubtless spent days. For every sin with which his book was blotted mine was doubtless blotted by a hundred, and yet at the end of it all this wise, good man trembled before the thought of the judgment, as had saints and philosophers before him for two thousand years—not so much at hell as at the Judgment. Was it perhaps not enlightenment, but a strange aphasia of a singularly foolish generation, which caused it to dismiss the Judgment as incredible? That is the terrible thing about those old verses and doctrines. If you analyse them, every word of them has its dreadful meaning, whereas with the modern clichés—Michael is quite right there—when you analyse them, they evaporate and are found to have no meaning.

'What are you thinking about?' asked Margaret.

'You would think I was dotty if I told you,' I answered.

'I do that anyway,' answered my disrespectful niece. 'Do for Heaven's sake come on, or we shall never be home for tea.'

XVI

It may appear to the reader (if reader there be) that I spent the whole of the war conducting interminable and indecent conversations in the West of England. I am far from denying that many others did more important work and accomplished more heroic feats than I. Yet it is not true that I did nothing. I worked hard at the War Office, even though the publication of what I did there is forbidden by the Defence of the Realm Act, and in any event it is no concern of this narrative. How infinite is our debt to Dora, who has sealed the lips of so many people anxious to tell stories almost intolerably boring of what they did in the war! But life in a Government department did at any rate teach me one thing. There are two sorts of writing. When an official announcement has to be made, it is obviously necessary that some half a dozen people should all have their whacks at the preparation of it. The reason, of course, is that what is required is an accurate version rather than an inspired version. So, too, in war-time every operational story must be submitted to censorship for security. That is inevitable, but it is also murderous to literature. Art is of its nature concerned with the unique, and a work of art must be the product of one mind. The artist may, if he will, submit his work to criticism, but he must retain in his own hands the right to accept or reject the criticism. The product of six pencils, the one cutting out here and another sub-editing there, each without reference to the other, can no more be a work of art than can be the stories in the cheap papers, where they let sub-editors hack around the contributors' copy. The proof is the product.

Now, if this principle that art can only come out of the brain of a single and free author be true in the secular world, it is equally true in the religious world. The Church, of course, is as right as are the Government departments to impose censorship and imprimaturs and every other guarantee on the official statements of its teaching. But it is not right if it seeks to impose such a restriction on the individual artist. The consequence of such a restriction must be to kill art. Truth is of the nature of poetry, not of mathematics. It is so many-sided that you kill the discovery of it if you attempt to hamper the artist by previous formulæ before he sets out upon his voyage of discovery.

Let me take an example. The greatest of all Christian poems is an expression of devotion by a married man to a lady who was not his wife. It is a profoundly moral and a profoundly Christian poem—Christian not only in that it expressed Christian truth, but in that it penetrated more deeply into Christian truth than any thinker had ever before penetrated. Had the theologians presumed to sit in judgment upon it, it must necessarily have been the lesser sitting in judgment upon the greater. Yet it is very hard to think of any three-line instruction to a censor which must not necessarily have laid down principles by which the *Divine Comedy* would have been condemned as immoral. There is a ludicrous quarter-truth in Tony Arbuthnot's absurdity that it, like, indeed, most other great works of art, is smut.

I know very little of history, but, as far as I can gather, the mediæval Church seems to have given a wise freedom and tolerance to artists. It is the post-Tridentine Church which is the Church of the Index and the imprimatur, and under their rule art, speculation and finally intellect all perish. Margaret tells me that Michael reads everything that he wants to read. But, if so, he does so only because he lives in a Protestant country, and, indeed, it is a most remarkable truth that, since the Council of Trent, all of the great Catholic literature that has been produced—with hardly, I think, the exception of one single book—has been produced by citizens of countries where the Government has been unfriendly to the Church—Protestant Germany, Protestant England, Protestant Holland, Protestant Switzerland or Liberal France.

That being so, I was not, I maintain, quite such a fool as Margaret thought me when I denied that my misunderstanding of Michael was purely one of prejudice. I do think that in these days of chaos and confusion the strong conservative force of the Roman Church, holding without fear to its traditional faith, refusing to be frightened into compromise by a passing fashion, is to be welcomed. It is an enormous advantage to a country that a reasonable proportion of its citizens should be Catholic, and so for that cause I would not upset Michael Paravane's faith even if I could, and I shall raise no objection if, as is likely enough, my niece should in time wish to join him in that faith. Yet if I were to become a Roman Catholic myself, then I should have to say that Roman Catholicism was God's unique revelation, and I should have, I suppose, to wish and pray that everybody should become a Roman Catholic, and that, were it to happen, would, it seems to me, spoil the whole virtue of the plan. Roman Catholics are a force making for liberty, for intelligence, for independence of mind—provided that there are a lot of other people who are not Roman Catholics.

'Oh, we shall not be allowed to have different books after the war,' said Michael one day in comic bitterness. 'There will just be one book which will be read aloud over the wireless by Sir William Beveridge.'

You get these valuable protests for freedom against totalitarian encroachment from Catholics in a non-Catholic country. But would they be allowed to make them, and do they ever make them, in a Catholic country? If ever they should have everything their own way, I would not trust them a yard. Michael says that it is absurd to ask whether religion favours literature, or democracy, or social reform. The question is whether literature or democracy or social reform favours religion. This is obviously logical if one is quite certain what is the religious truth—as obviously unhelpful if one is still in search for it. What was good enough for Peter was a stumbling-block for Pilate. Michael also says something about the Church as a body and much more than the sum of the individuals which compose it—and that I must confess that I do not understand. He also says that I know nothing about Catholic countries—which is profoundly true.

With these reservations, then, I found Michael Paravane an extremely refreshing influence in my life. I never took up again with him is the discussion of his religious beliefs. Where you do not agree with a person but like him and wish to work with him, it is best that he should state his faith once and for all so that one may understand, in so far as one is capable of understanding, and then leave it. There is no profit in going over the ground again and again. But I had great hopes from his political influence. For the spirit of generosity, let it blow whence it may, is what we so sadly need to-day. Though he was Bobby's political opponent, yet I felt that in a manner the mantle of Bobby had descended upon him—and it was characteristic of Bobby that his mantle should descend as easily upon a political opponent as upon a political friend. For each was really both a true Liberal and a true Conservative. Bobby was a Conservative who believed in the conservation of all traditional institutions—among them the Liberal Party. Michael was a Liberal who believed in the toleration of all tolerable men—among them Conservatives.

I did not know very much about the country until I took on the task of doing what I could to help Ruth to keep her family and my own family together in the difficult circumstances of the war. The chief contrast that struck me between the moral atmosphere of town and country life was that, as Ruth said, life in the town is so much more lonely. There is an inevitable absence of neighbourliness in the town. One probably does not know the inhabitant of the next flat or of the house next door. Even if one knows him, one's own business is at distance from one's home, and therefore the friends of home do not know the ins and outs of one's business troubles. Business acquaintances know nothing of one's home life. In the country all is more of a piece.

I am not concerned to deny that there are disadvantages in this—that there is something to be said, at any rate upon occasions, against being too much overlooked. I am only concerned as a reporter from the outside to record facts. Certainly Ruth's brave experiment was only possible because of the assistance of her neighbours. The other farmers treated her neither as a landlord nor as a competitor, but as a colleague. They were ever ready to lend her tools and machines, and, what is more, to offer to lend them. The labour problem of modern mechanised agricultural life is that only a small skilled staff is required for the greater part of the year, but it is desirable at harvest-time to add unskilled but willing labour to this skeleton. In the war years, naturally enough, everyone was overworked, and yet Ruth's non-farming neighbours, whenever they had an hour to spare, in haymaking or in harvest-time always gave it to Ruth.

Doubtless this helpfulness was to some extent the response of chivalry to Ruth's widowhood—the belated tribute to Bobby's popularity. But to a large extent it was simply the traditional habit of a happy village. In particular I was struck by the extraordinary loyalty of the men on the farm—chief and first among them, of course, Billy Perkins. I was always interested to notice that, though Armstrong was for ever prating to the villagers of the good things that would be theirs if only they had their rights, yet he was not particularly popular with them. To some of them he was a bore and to others he was a joke. The reasons for their aversion from radicalism were, I fancy, two. First, they had a very admirable hatred of envy as the most odious and unchristian of qualities—a sense, like Ulysses in *Troilus and Cressida,* that appetite was 'a universal wolf' which, if 'doubly seconded with will and power,' would 'make a universal prey and last eat up itself.' In other words, they wisely thought that a world in which all were encouraged to indulge, and did indulge, indiscriminately their appetites would come to a bad end. The elders thought this because they were inheritors of a traditional wisdom. The younger generation under the divorcing influence of modern education had perhaps learnt less of traditional wisdom than their fathers, but the universal wolf stalked too evidently through the world to require any book-learning to teach the danger of the surrender to appetite. Yet hatred of envy was not the only cause of their suspicion of reform. They saw very clearly that all these reforms which Armstrong and others advocated could only be put into practice by the Government, and for the Government they had an ineradicable suspicion. It was a townee's Government that had let them down in the past and would let them down again. They would sooner be without the benefits than have any more dealings with the Government. 'We've got our place, and we've got our work,' Billy Perkins said one day to Armstrong, 'and if we're always gabbling about our place there's no time left to do our work.' The retort was generally held to be a just one. Armstrong's gift of words did him no good with the villagers, for they felt that a too fluent arguer used words as a weapon with which to bludgeon them out of their opinions. They refused to budge save at arguments that came at the slow pace of their own minds.

It would be a fantastic misjudgment which would call any of such men a snob. Billy Perkins, for instance, accepted the order of things—what Shakespeare called 'degree.' He made no attempt to assert himself on fields in which he was incompetent, not through false humility but through the very proper pride which knows that it has no need to do so. He was a cowman first and, when needed, a ploughman, and when cows or ploughs were in question he knew that he was the equal of his sovereign, his opinion as valuable as any man's. He could thus afford to allow to others the honour where their honour was due. His loyalty he did not owe primarily to any man but to the land for the service of which he lived. And if after Bobby's death he gave to Ruth service even perhaps a little more nearly whole-hearted, in the most literal sense, than he had given to Bobby in easier days, that was because he who serves the land is made thereby to be also one of nature's very perfect gentlemen.

But there was in him no shadow of false servility to those who claimed to be his betters through an accident of birth. He tolerated me, I think, but merely because I had humility. By the accident of time I came to him in genuine humility. I happened to make his real friendship at the time when the death of Bobby and Marjorie, the general suffering of the war, had shown me how superficial and insufficient was my previous philosophy—at a time when I was truly anxious to learn from people wiser than myself. I came to learn, and he was willing to teach—explicitly about the land, implicitly about all the lessons of life. He approved of Marigold Arbuthnot though she knew nothing about the land; indeed, because she knew nothing about the land and made no pretence to do so. He found in her the root virtues. 'She'll make a good wife to Mr. George,' he said. But when Tony Arbuthnot, who had by then got some sort of job in the Ministry of Agriculture, came bouncing along to explain his new policy of 'milk before meat,' it was a very different story. 'It does not matter about the cows calving,' engagingly explained Tony. 'All that we want is that they should have milk.'

'Mothers don't give milk, Mr. Arbuthnot, to please the Board of Agriculture,' bluntly replied Billy, 'and it's the same with cows. You can't deal unnatural with cows, and it would be better if you didn't try to deal unnatural with people. Cows have milk, the same as women, because they have children to give it to. If you want more milk, you send the cows to bull, and don't talk silly.'

It was blunt and it was final. A more pompous man would have found it unforgivable. But Tony, who, though he was a fraud, at least had the grace to know that he was a fraud, only laughed.

The company of these country folk brought to me a

growing conviction which led at last to a strange experience. There lived down the lane a grubby, kindly old man—an old day-jobbing labourer called William. He would sometimes come in to set up a new chicken run or the like. He was a decent, friendly old man, particularly kind to the children, for whom he used to cut mock flowers out of carrots. His children were all grown up, and he lived alone with his wife in a rather dirty cottage.

This January his wife had fallen ill and had gone into the hospital at Bristol for treatment. In the evenings William would come round from his lonely little cottage to telephone through to the hospital for a report. I remember him very well one evening standing by the open front door in the hall. He fiddled with his cloth cap in his left hand. His face had suddenly hollowed and sunken, and there was a frightened look in his eyes as of a trapped animal. 'She's not so good to-night,' he said in answer to our inquiries. In truth, the news had been, as we knew, desperately bad.

He pulled himself together, put down his cap and started to fumble in his right-hand pocket for the fivepence to pay for the call. He held out the coppers. Ruth, of course, waved them away.

'Of course, that's all right, William,' she said.

Martin at the same time turned on the outside light that lit up the porch. It was in every violation of the black-out regulations that he did so, but there was in him an anarchic strain which made it a pleasure to violate regulations. He disliked the air-raid warden—a silly little fussy village schoolmaster. Nor did we worry so much about black-out in the country and well inland in 1944 as we had done in 1940.

The light shone behind William's back; and the whole scene stamped itself with a curious effect upon my mind. I felt that I was present at a scene of symbolism. We have all of us read pious old mediæval stories which tell how the master of the house, when he entertains a stranger, finds that he has been entertaining Christ unawares. We have dismissed such tales as meaningless sentimentalities. I cannot better describe my discovery when I saw William thus in his distress than by saying that I then for the first time in a measure understood those stories.

Let me try to explain what I mean and what I do not mean. God knows that, like Voltaire, *je ne suis né pour célébrer les saints.* But, if hagiography is not my forte, neither is it here my purpose. I do not mean—let me, to begin with, make it entirely clear—that I thought that William was an entirely Christ-like character. I did not, to tell the truth, know very much about him. I had not often seen him before, and up to this moment I have never seen him again. He was indeed, they said, a drunken old rascal, and, although I liked his kindness and his fidelity, I had no reason at all to think that here was a character without fault—the ideal man. My meaning is quite a different one. I know no theology, so I cannot say whether my belief is orthodox or whether it is sensible. But for what it is worth I try to set it down.

Throughout these last few years—the only years of my life during which I can seriously pretend that I have ever tried to think—I have been haunted by the doctrine of original sin. In the understanding of that doctrine lies, it seems to me, the one possibility of an understanding of any of the problems of human nature. Without such an understanding no virtue, not even charity—at least, any intellectual exercise of it—is possible. Now, the first step in the formulation of the doctrine of original sin is simple and incontrovertible. Man is clearly corrupt. We do not need much circumspection to find the monuments in support of this. Nor do even the Rousseauan denials of this deny the point at issue. There may or may not have been at some other time a noble savage who was free from corruption, just as there may or may not have once been an as yet unfallen Adam. With that speculation I am not at the moment concerned. I am concerned with man as he is here and now. He is imperfect and capable of corruption. It may be, if you care to argue so, institutions or art or civilisations which have corrupted him. These are words. Whatever the corrupting influence, it could never have found entrance unless there had been some inherent weakness in man which gave it entrance. Therefore man is in himself liable to err.

Yet man, unlike other creatures, while he is liable to err, is also able to recognise error—even in himself. The piston-rod cracks, but it does not know that it has failed when it cracks. The horse strives to win the race, but as far as we know, it is only in obedience to some animal instinct that he runs. He does not understand what it is all about. But man has a double nature and a double picture of himself. He sees himself as he is, but he also sees himself—he has a dim vision of himself—as he ought to be, as God made him to be. And it is the latter which, though it be the unreal picture as far as the passing accident of this world goes, is yet ultimately the truer picture. There was that truth in the metaphor of the Platonists that we were living in a cave and seeing only the shadows of reality which the light reflected on to the wall in front of us. And, whatever my difficulties about belief in hell, I have never, since I started to think at all, had any difficulty about belief in purgatory. For that whole doctrine seems to me utterly congruent to common sense. The I-as-I-am is a defacement, blotted and smudged, of the I-as-God-made-me, and since nothing worse than God made it to be can enjoy the company of God, the blots must in some way, whatever the precise reality behind the metaphor, be erased and purged away before I am fit to meet Him. It is no more hard to see the need for purgatory than it is hard to see why the schoolboy ought to be made to wash his face before he goes in to see his godfather.

'Then we shall see face to face.' But is there any way in which we can penetrate through to the vision of things as they are—even now—when, as a habit, we see but through a glass darkly? I have written of my discovery of Dante, and it was from Dante that I learnt the first answer to this question. We can see things as they are, Dante tells us, in romantic love. The Beatrice whom he sees and loves is not the stained Beatrice of everyday life, but the Beatrice of the Beatific Vision. Love is not blind. Rather it is love alone which sees—which catches the vision of the truth behind the shadow. If love can do this, all beauty also can in a measure do it. It is a folly of Keats to erect his dictum of 'Beauty is Truth' into an alternative to a metaphysics or a religion. Without an explanation it is obviously untrue. The objector has merely to point to one of the many uglinesses of earth to refute it. But in its metaphysical background it may well be true. What we see as ugly may well seem so only because we do not see it in its proper place in the whole picture. That which is in place is beautiful, and, if we could see all, all would be seen to be in place. Thus beauty is truth in a sense in which ugliness is not truth, and when we see a thing as beautiful we see it as it really is and in its proper place.

If these claims be true, then there is a third vision, which is akin to the vision of romantic love and the vision of beauty, though not quite the same as either the one or the other of them. We sometimes have the feeling that a person's action in a particular circumstance was exactly right. This was just, we feel, what God must have wished him to do. For the moment at any rate the gap between the man-as-he-is and the man-as-God-made-him is closed and, looking at the actual, we find ourselves looking straight into the ultimate. That is what I feel that I was looking on in this curious scene with William in the hall, the light shining behind him like a grotesque mock-halo that did not quite fit. To plough the land, to do odd jobs, to pay for one's telephone calls, to love one's wife, to hope for company in the closing years and to accept it without repining when the hope is denied—it all seemed exactly right, a picture of utter fidelity and the pattern of faithful men around him. I looked into the eyes of things as they ought to be and learnt there the secret of how all men are two, just as Dante learnt it in the eyes of Beatrice or as every lover learns it in the eyes of the beloved. In a way the discovery is more wholly intellectual and therefore more nearly explicable when, as in a discovery of purely moral admiration, it is untinged with emotion. You remember Langland?

> He who is true of tongue, and with his two hands
> Who works with this will, and wishes no evil,
> Is a God, says the Gospel, on our ground and in heaven
> And likened to Our Lord in St. Luke's teaching.

That is what life is like. Of the special visions of the mystics Heaven knows that I have had no experience and am not likely to have experience this side the tomb. But the life of this world is, as it were, a tissue-paper stretched over reality through which we can see the dim form of reality behind, and to all of us there come every now and again glimpses of the true picture seen through little rents in the paper. The occasions of these glimpses there is no foretelling—a child's smile, a peasant's unshaven face beneath the light, a gracious bow, the scream of a shell, a 'chorus-ending in Euripides'—but they come to all men, and Michael says—and I am sure rightly—that only those who have blinded themselves by their denial of the possibility of the vision fail to perceive the reality of it. These claims only seem at all extraordinary because we live in a sort of age of atrophy.

The next morning, as I was climbing the fence with the children in order to get up on to the hill from which one gets the great view of the village nestling in the cup beneath us and then on beyond that the whole plain of Sedgemoor stretching out to the west like an endless, unruffled sea, old Hands and Billy Perkins came by, Hands looking for his sheep. He had just heard from Billy Perkins of Tony Arbuthnot's agricultural theories. Hands was something of a 'know-all,' and was shocked by the sheer ignorance of Tony, but Billy's grievance went deeper. To Billy it was a shame to hold forth on that of which one knew nothing. But, beyond that, Tony's views had shocked him by more than their ignorance. There was about them what Bobby used to call 'a contempt for fecundity'—which, though he could not have put his thought in such words, Billy Perkins would have felt to be a mark of a dying age. Bobby was never tired of explaining how the rhythm of a happy life needed the mark of fecundity—large families, large litters of animals, heavy crops on the fields, the trees weighed down with fruit. It may be that it was Billy Perkins from whom he learnt this faith. For certainly Billy, in his inarticulate fashion, had it as well as he. When people talked of the restriction of production, Billy would listen and approve in so far as the motive was to preserve the fertility of the land. But if the motive was a purely financial one, and crops or calves or eggs were to be restricted in order to raise prices, then he would sadly shake his head.

Hands took up the tale. He was a great believer in heredity and scorned deeply those who, as he put it, 'did not reckon of blood.' He told me that it was only the poor shepherd who was indifferent to the blood of his sheep dog. He himself would never use a dog that he had not trained himself and with whose pedigree he was not acquainted. Once in his life, when he was a young man, he had made the mistake of indifference and he had learnt his lesson. A farmer over by Cary had a litter of five pups and begged Hands to take one. Hands knew the mother, who was a good sheep dog, but he did not know the father. His first instinct was to refuse, but he allowed himself to be over-persuaded and took the dog. Hands had to keep the dog for six months before it was old enough for breaking-in. Then he started to train it. It proved quick to learn and at first it seemed that all would be well. But then one day the lambs were put into a field that was half clover and half rape and where it was necessary to keep them off the rape and on the clover. The dog would not do his job and again and again allowed the lambs to wander on to the rape. At last, losing his temper, Hands threw his crook at the dog. At this insult the dog at once gave up his work and came back and sat in sulkiness behind his master. Nor from that day forward would he ever again do any sheep work. He had to be sold for rabbiting, nor was it until after the sale that Hands learnt the explanation. The dog was not a pure sheep dog. His father had had retriever's blood in him. Hands admitted that he himself was at fault in losing his temper with a dog, but his primary fault was to have traffic at all for a sheep dog with one that was not of pure sheep-dog blood.

'One dog's good for one thing,' he said, 'and one for another. But I'll never again break a dog that isn't pure bred. The same with humans.'

I found the challenge, I must confess, just a trifle embarrassing. For my own mother was Kentucky and my father Lowland Scot, and my father, a successful business man, was yet a self-made man. He had sent me to Eton, and I have mixed much of my life with gentlemen. Yet I am not myself quite a gentleman. I married above my station.

Everyone talks of such things behind a man's back, but

it is often thought embarrassing if he speaks quite frankly about his own social origin. I do not know why, for it is both important and interesting. There are great advantages in being, to some extent, as I am, both *déraciné* and *déclassé*—brought up in one class, by descent of another. Many of my schoolfellows would have found themselves in social isolation in the life of motor-salesman at Wolverhampton, which I lived, after going down from Oxford. I found no difficulty in it, any more than I found difficulty in returning to the club when I came up to London. So to-day I think that I may justly boast that I can pass from class to class more easily than those who are more fixedly of a class. It is of indifference to me if I eat in the dining-room or the kitchen.

But, while there is gain in thus sitting loose to one's origins, there is also—I know it well—loss. Man is not strong enough to stand alone. Certainly I am not strong enough to stand alone. A man needs many loyalties to help him in his effort. He should have many things which he would be ashamed to disgrace—a name handed down from honoured fathers, a home with house, hills, fields familiar and loved, a wife, a hope of posterity, a trade that is a vocation and which has its own honour to be guarded, the love of beauty. This nomadic world, in which so many millions wander by compulsion and in which many even of those who are not compelled move restlessly from place to place and from home to home, is also a breaking world. Man is a plant that cannot grow without its roots. I wondered if Hands was thinking how much of all that I lacked and pitying me accordingly—thinking 'a dog that isn't pure bred—the same with humans.' Or am I right to comfort myself that with humans what counts is not mere blood but upbringing? The demand for the pure breed smacks surely too much of Nazi-ism.

The two old men hambled off with a sad good-morning,

and I was left alone with my children leaning on the stile and looking down upon the village, upon the smoke spiralling up from Ruth's chimney, upon the village church with the wool-tower and the Abbot's Arms beside it, upon the Manor with its park now filled with busy American lorries, upon Vanity Fair and all the world.

> I saw the smoke-hued hamlets, quaint
> With Westland King and Westland saint,
> And watched the western glory faint
> Along the road to Frome.

Like Piers Plowman, I had been 'through this world to witness wonders,' and, like him, 'I saw strange sights like scenes of faerie.' If you look down on life from a height you have a sense that the creatures below you are toys, moved about by a Master Hand and for a purpose beyond their guessing. Viewed thus the scene is indeed a scene of faerie, of an interpenetrated world where forces that are from outside it are for ever playing their battling part. It is a stage, but the stage is not all existence. A figure that looked like Hawkes, the policeman, rode down the hill opposite on a bicycle. A horse and cart clod-clomped up it. Too much of such a bird's-eye meditation would lead one to folly and fatalism, but a little of it is good for the soul. Things are seen most truly when they are seen from a certain distance. The lesson to be learnt is not the lesson of Omar Khayyam or Thomas Hardy, but rather the two great complementary faiths—that there is a pattern and a purpose, and that the pattern is quite different from any that the actors in it can guess. 'We have erected a banner to which the wise and the brave can repair; the event is in the hand of God.'

The church clock struck twelve across the valley.

'It's twelve, Daddy,' said Christopher, 'and you promised that you would play with us when it struck twelve.'

'Very well,' I said, 'what shall we play?'

'I don't think we will play,' said Monica a little pompously. 'The tractor has come this morning. We ought to go and inspect it.'

'Oh, let's play,' said Christopher.

'One doesn't really need to play when things come,' said Monica.

'I wonder if the horses are glad or sorry now that there's a tractor to do the ploughing,' said Christopher.

'I should be glad if I were a horse,' said Monica.

'I should be sorry,' said Christopher.

XVII

A FEW days later I heard my children debating a little ungraciously which they liked the better of their two male cousins. Robert received the vote of both of them. This was, perhaps, a little hard on Martin, for Martin certainly paid them every bit as much attention as was at all good for them. But children, of course, judge by familiarity. They knew Robert better because he had been with them regularly all the school holidays, while Martin had passed entirely out of their life during the time that he was in the Mediterranean War, and they saw him now only on hurried leaves. Besides, the favourite game of the moment was an elaborate war game, the precise details of which I never mastered, but where the general idea was that the grown-ups were posted as strategic points at various positions in the orchard, while the young, in their capacity of mobile troops, rushed wildly about on ponies waving sticks. Robert was extraordinarily good and patient at playing this interminable and appalling game with them, as indeed also was

Margaret. Martin's enthusiasm for it was a trifle more tepid—intelligibly tepid.

'Cousin Martin doesn't want to play the war-game,' complained Christopher.

'Oh, Cousin Martin has fought in the real war,' explained Monica in tones of some contempt, as if that was a misfortune to which no gentleman would call attention.

It is recorded that, when they invited Alexander the Great to listen to a singer whose voice was like the nightingale's, Alexander replied, 'I have heard the nightingale itself.' Martin's feelings towards the war-game were, I fancy, much the same. He did play once or twice, and when he refused he always refused graciously. But he liked to spend his time on leave reading. On this leave he was ploughing through Dryden's *Absalom and Achitophel*, and I do not think that he can be fairly blamed for his refusal to play.

As I say, I do not pretend to have mastered the intricacies of the game. But, roughly, a certain area in the orchard was marked out with whiting to represent Italy. At various points within that area various objects were posted to mark the major cities—the old apple-tree was Bari, the wheelbarrow Brindisi. The dog's dinner-plate was Palermo, and I was Naples. Ruth was appointed to be Rome, but, as she had to go off to peel the potatoes, the Eternal City was with us only in spirit during all but the first opening moves of the campaign. Off-shore George had to move up and down, puffing like a steam-engine, to represent the British Navy. He was selected for this responsibility on the ground that a clerical collar looked like a funnel. From time to time rotten apples, to represent bombs, were thrown at objects of interest, such as, for instance, the city of Naples. But the greater part of the fighting, in defiance of fashion, was conducted by cavalry. Monica and Christopher rode about on their Shetland ponies, waving great sticks around their heads and occasionally lashing out with them with a somewhat terrifying vagueness. Robert was the Germans, and his duty was to run away and from time to time to get captured. Wobbles, the ginger cat, was the Pope, and her kittens were all cardinals. Far from being a prisoner of the Vatican, Wobbles, alone of all the actors, was free to wander at will over land and sea and had no official duties.

Doubtless it was a good game, but it was also January. Being Naples was, after about forty minutes, extremely cold work. Would it never come to an end?

'They also serve who only stand and wait,' I remarked to George as the British Navy steamed past my battered sea-front.

'*O passi graviora, dabit Deus his quoque finem,*' consolingly replied George.

'Uncle George, you're supposed to be right up off Nettuno—right up here,' complained Monica, pointing at a repulsive molehill fifty yards away.

George proved right. Bertha and the welcome gong at last called us to lunch, and a truce of God was declared in honour of roast beef and Yorkshire pudding.

A fire of beech-logs crackled in the grate.

'Beech sends out sparks,' complained Bertha. 'You ought only to burn oak or ash—that's to say, if you can't have fruit-wood.'

She held it almost as a grievance against Mr. Bevin that you could not both use the apple-tree for firewood and also have it bear apples. In an ampler world there would be both apples and apple-wood in plenty for the gentry. To me in my urban ignorance firewood was little more than firewood, and I was ignorant of the subtle differences with which Bertha's mind was filled.

'The more slow-growing the tree, the more lastingly it burns,' Ruth told me.

I found myself silent and pensive at lunch in the midst of a howling and yelling bear-garden. I was thinking of George's quotation. It spoke of deeper truths than the coming of lunch-time—that line wherein pagan literature comes perhaps most close to the expression of the Christian hope, and indeed of the Christian certainty, the faith that, though no man can say how, yet somehow goodness will do good, courage will prove worth while and suffering will have an end. I do not believe those who seek to comfort us with pictures of peace and security, of a world at ease and contentment, as soon as this war is finished. Such tales are for buffoons. It is a world of sweat and tears and what is all too likely to be a world of blood to which I have brought my children. I am not sorry that they should be born into such a hard, turbulent world—a world with frost on the ground and a keen, nipping wind blowing in from the Atlantic. I owe them no apology. They are better in such a world, armed only with faith in the final purposes, than was their father twenty-five years ago in his metallic world of nescience and the promise of immediate Utopia, of the brotherhood of man in theory and universal hatred in practice, of the puerilities, the complacencies and the despairs. Christopher the other day was reading some adventure story for boys and complaining that it was 'soppy,' because at the last the hero emerged from his hair-breadth escapes and all 'lived happily ever after.' He preferred, it seems, like Hardy, a hanging at the last.

'But that's how things are,' said Monica.

I know not what God of chance can have put it into her head to say these words—so profoundly true, but true only in a sense much deeper than ten years old can have ever guessed. For though Monica can hardly yet have known it, our fortress, like Mansoul, cannot be captured save with its defender's own consent. The defeatist has by his very title abandoned his faith in courage and goodness and defeated himself. His despair is the sin for which there is no forgiveness. For there is good at the heart of things, and to him that endures there shall come at last an end.

Like the dead in Rupert Brooke, I have 'gone proudly friended.' My happy lot has fallen among people better and wiser than myself. Bobby Fossett, my wife, my sister Ruth, George, Michael Paravane—I know that in them there were reserves of character and wisdom from which, had I not drawn, I could hardly have escaped from my undergraduate crudities. Of all the gospels, the most dreary is the gospel of youth—that which claims the world as the heritage of the young. Of all discoveries, the most delightful is that one does grow wiser with age—with age and the company of wise men. How right the Chinese are to reverence age! I can see, for instance, how both Martin and Margaret grow both in wisdom and virtue as they grow in maturity, and, as they grow, I find in them, too, since they are of more rooted stock than I, a deeper understanding than I find in myself. And there, too, I can often now go gladly to school, where a few years ago I was still an instructing uncle. One grows, too, with age and wisdom less snobbish, for one ceases to be concerned with class in its economic and political aspect. If I have learnt wisdom from George or from Robert Fossett, I have learnt it also from Billy Perkins and from the other men and women of the land, Ruth's neighbours, men and women of an extraordinary kindliness and an extraordinary virtue, living hourly in the company of the basic miracle of growth. Never again shall I be guilty of the impudence of the callow young radical who thought that he was better off than such people because he had a little more money than they and who considered that it would be a reform to make them more like himself. I am not quite sure whether something like this is what Michael has in mind when he speaks of the 'communion of saints.' If so, odd as the phrase sounds in our secularised day, I think that I begin to understand what he means. Virtue, luckily for me, is a contagious disease.

George and I were talking at lunch about Virgil and that great line of his.

'It's just like Virgil's diabolical cleverness,' said George, 'to make Æneas say that line and then explain that he does not really believe it himself.'

'How do you mean?' I asked.

'If you remember the passage,' said George, 'it's in the first book of the *Æneid*. Æneas and his followers had been hurled back on to the African coast by a storm just when they thought that they were going to make Italy. Æneas does not really think that there is any hope for them, Virgil explains. He really thinks that their number is up, but he just says this to encourage them.'

'He says it, thinking it isn't true, and it really is true,' said Ruth.

'Exactly,' said George. 'That is obviously Virgil's view. Æneas particularly—and all of us to some extent—are men of destiny. In our high moments God uses us for purposes beyond our understanding. The outcomes are hidden from us, but we say and we do more than we know. And our task is to be waiting and ready to obey and co-operate.'

> 'But we, like sentries, are obliged to stand
> On starless nights and wait the appointed hour,'

said Martin. 'Daddy always used to be quoting that.'

'Exactly,' said George. 'In many ways Dryden was the most Virgilian of all English poets—in mind, I mean. Of course, this being used for purposes beyond oneself is a very attractive faith for a poet—a chap who is always scribbling things down and never quite sure whether they are tommy-rot or the profoundest revelation of truth undreamed of.'

'But that's just it,' said Ruth, turning round from the sink, where she was by now heavily engaged with the washing-up. 'If Æneas said more than he himself understood, so, too, did Virgil.'

'How do you mean?' asked George.

'Well, Virgil thought,' said Ruth, 'that in spite of everything Æneas was going to get to Italy and Rome to be founded and to conquer the known world and to be ruled in peace by Augustus. The world after a few years of such rule would be so different from what it had ever been before that you could not unfairly tell a child born then that he was born into a new age. But he had no notion what child was going to be born or how the Roman world was going to fulfil her destiny.'

With all her many accomplishments, I had never before thought of Ruth as a Virgilian critic, but there seemed to me a great deal of truth in this judgment from the soap-suds.

'Very true,' I said, 'but where do we go from here, then? Virgil sees that there is more to it than Æneas guessed, and we see that there is more to it than Virgil guessed, and doubtless somebody else sees that there is more to it than we guessed.'

'Doubtless,' said George. 'But what does it matter? It is not as if the original hope was proved untrue. It was only proved more true. The last word is still with hope, and somehow or other the gentle things win in the end.'